LIVING SPRINGS PUBLISHERS
PRESENTS:

STORIES THROUGH THE AGES
BABY BOOMERS PLUS
2019

Compiled and edited by:
Henry E. Peavler, Dan Peavler, and Jacqueline Veryle Peavler

Introduction by Henry Peavler and Dan Peavler

Living Springs Publishers

Each story in this collection is a work created from the imagination or experience of the author. The views expressed in the stories do not necessarily reflect the views of Living Spring Publishers L.L.P.

Living Springs Publishers
www.LivingSpringsPublishers.com

Cover design by Jacqueline Peavler

Cover Image:
Copyright: <a href='https://www.123rf.com/profile_sakkmesterke'>sakkmesterke / 123RF Stock Photo</a>

Dedicated to Apollo 11 and all the history we experienced - to those who made history, those who remember it and those who write about it.

Table of Contents

Synopses

Joanne M. Kuhns has won first prize in the 2019 Baby Boomers Plus contest. Her wonderful story, '**Payday at the Mountaineers Café**' is told through the eyes of Lindy, a little girl in the early 1960's, who tries very hard to make sense of the strange things adults say and do. Lindy's perceptions, rooted in her innocence, are often funny and poignant.

Ronald C. Milburn has captured second place in this years' contest for "**Paddys Tonsorial Emporium**". Paddy is a likeable barber in a small town that could be located in any state in the Union. The story is told through the eyes of the shoe-shine boy, George, who is privy to the gossip, rumors and inside information from the town elite who use Paddys as a gathering place. Don't miss this beautifully written story.

Henry Stevens survives the depression and all the other difficulties of life that a small farmer must face. Yet the one thing he longs for eludes him until the very end, only is it too late to matter? David Tarpenning wins third place for his touching tribute to human perseverance with his story, "**Now would be Forever**".

A hilarious romp through the mind of a fifth-grade girl and the school play where she has been slighted, horribly and unfairly by Sister Mary Agnes. In "**Revolt of the Blessed Virgin Mother**", Mary Alice Dixon has crafted an exceptional story both funny and believable. Life isn't always fair, but our heroine does her part to get even for the slights she suffers. Delightful reading.

Big brother gets a new puppy yet, most of the chores fall to little sister who performs them willingly but always knowing that the dog is his. Jamie Enslin's family tale, "**The Dog's His**", is well written and a joy to read.

In Jackie Ross Flaum's story "**The Narcissist**" former Germantown, TN. alderman Dan Anderson died of poison from the bulbs of the Narcissus poeticus flower. A poetic end for a classic narcissist, but was it an accident—or something else?

Nothing grabs your attention like a living nativity scene on a cold Christmas evening. Maybe Jay Gilbert's experience at the "**St. Paul's Living Nativity**" carries that emotion to an extreme but we, the reader, are the better for it. Wonderful tale of one family's night of fame in the living nativity.

Lisa McCormack has written a wonderfully witty story about a young girl coming of age during a difficult time in her life and the life of her loved ones. "**Trouble with Blooming**" describes a seemingly idyllic existence shattered by events that expose the ugly side of human nature to our heroine, Louise, who faces each crisis with the dogged determination of youth. A must read.

A freak snowstorm and a little serendipity offers a chance at romance and reward as coincidental travelers come together during "**A Night in St. Louis**". This wonderful story was written by Race McKee.

"**Reelect the President**" by Anthony J. Mohr, is required reading for anyone who lived through the Nixon Presidency and everyone else who needs to learn the lessons gained. This is real inside information and a part of the story never told. Don't miss this wonderfully written account of one man's brush with the infamy of the Nixon years.

I.M. Merckel's charming story, "**The Teacher**" is a feel-good tale about a curmudgeonly traveler who spends more time in airports than at home, or so it seems. He finds fault with most of the people and situations around him until one special relationship develops that he can't ignore and the result is a wonderful lesson learned. Great story!

Lt. Col. Robert B. Robeson, USA (Ret) has crafted an emotional description of what a medical evacuation helicopter pilot experienced during the war in Vietnam. "**Life and Death in Vietnam**" leaves the reader breathless at the intensity of the action. How did these men survive? This story is marvelously written and stated in the clear, no-nonsense mood of the times. A must read.

A young man grows up on an idyllic mountain range, living the cowboy life that he longed for. Only not every experience was pleasant. Even the worst disaster imaginable led to life's lessons learned and a successful happy adult. Don't miss Matthew Tredway's "**Tincup, Colorado 1982**".

"**The Ring**" is a story of an elite hairdresser, an act of love between a long-time client — a promise, an expensive diamond ring against a promise of the heart and the power of hair. Trudy Wells-Meyer wrote this story with a belief: "One does not choose the time to write . . . it chooses you."

Patricia Walkow's story "**Woven**" is a delightful story of a middle-aged couple whose lives are affected by a seemingly impossible event that causes them to reflect on a relationship grown stale over time. Did it really happen? Only they know for sure and that is all that matters.

Introduction

Winston Churchill once said, "History will be kind to me because I intend to write it." History is most often thought of as important earth-shattering moments in time, such as the lunar landing in 1969, to which this book is dedicated. But on a personal level our lives are shaped by incidents that may not affect anyone but ourselves. The authors for "Stories Through the Ages Baby Boomers Plus 2019" have given us a marvelous glimpse into many of those moments, some embarrassing, some terrifying, some funny, but all of them poignant and readily identifiable as human emotions we have all experienced in the course of our lives. The stories we received from across our great nation help to preserve these memories so that they become a record of the past.

We at Living Springs Publishers wish to thank all the talented and creative authors who sent in stories. We believe these stories help to define history. From the viewpoint of a shoeshine boy in a barbershop; to a medivac pilot surviving with tenacity during the Viet Nam war; to several stories seen through the eyes of a child, our authors prove to the readers that the past is not made up of only facts and figures, but of memories and experiences.

We allow authors freedom to write about any subject they choose, whether fiction or non-fiction. Part of the fun of being a judge is wondering, 'did that really happen?'. We are constantly amazed at the number of passionate, quality writers who send in their stories. As our contest grows, we receive more and more submissions making the judging difficult. We are forced to choose between excellent stories knowing that one author will be elated and another disappointed. We can only include 15 or 16 stories in each book. We received many, many excellent submissions, but the nature of the contest allows only a few winners. Thank you to everyone who sent a story and to all the readers, the true beneficiaries of these pages. There are a lot of short-story contests out there. Don't give up even if you aren't published. Your writings will be a legacy for you, your family and the readers of the world.

We are conscious of the importance of storytelling and the gift the authors provide to the reader. History means different things to different people, the personal memories of our lives are a big part of our history, maybe more so than the momentous events. We believe that a true account of the past will help shape a better future, so keep writing.

Congratulations to all the authors included in this year's book. Enjoy all the stories and be sure to read the biographies of the authors at the end of their section

Payday at the Mountaineer's Café
BY JOANNE M. KUHNS

"Lindy, would you like to pull out the choke for me?"

I nodded, unable to say a word. Only my sister Trudy, who recently became old enough to drive by herself, had been allowed to do that up till now, not even my ten-year-old big brother Kevin. I slid across the big bench seat closer to Mom, reached for the dashboard and gently pulled on the knob labeled "CHOKE." As she turned the key, the car sputtered to life and we sat for a bit until the engine ran smoothly.

"All right, push it back in now."

I did and felt that I was now nearly an expert on auto mechanics. We were in our used 1956 Ford, made the year I was born. Mom said she picked this car because Daddy, who did not move here with us from Detroit, worked for Chrysler. Our car was light blue on the bottom with a white roof and white seats inside. I was sure it was the most elegant car in the world, even though there was a spot on the back seat where Kitty had peed. Now that it was finally summertime, it meant that on some Wednesday nights we would all pile into our pretty car and go to the Moonlight Drive-In on "Buck-It" night, where it cost one dollar for one carload of people to see two movies, no matter how many kids and dogs were squished into the car, including the trunk.

Today we were on Mom's weekly trip to the Mountaineer's Café to collect her waitressing pay from the manager. This was one of the lucky days when I got to go with her. Not only that, but neither Trudy nor Kevin was along, so I got to sit in the front seat with Mom, which felt very grownup.

After we'd gone a few blocks, I realized that for once I had the entire car, front and back, all to myself, other than Mom. I alternated between sitting in the front seat, curling up on the floor under the glovebox, or swinging myself over to the long bench seat in the back and waving to the driver behind us through the rear window. When Kevin did that stuff Mom usually yelled at him, but today she didn't even notice.

"Good heavens, Lindy, get up here with me and sit still."

Mom sounded like she might get angry after all, so I hopped into the front again and sat quietly. She always seemed to go to the Mountaineer's Café with one of us kids at lunchtime, which was good for me today because I was especially hungry. The sunlight grew warmer, so I cranked down my window and put my arm out to feel the wind rush between my fingers as we drove. I was wearing my shorts, shirt and sandals, and would climb our front yard tree when we got home to look for bird nests. I liked robins' nests the most of all because they had blue eggs.

I looked at Mom to see if she'd tell me to pull my arm back in, but she was staring straight ahead and tapping her fingers on the steering wheel really hard. She had on a turtleneck sweater, which she usually only wore in winter, and a skirt and nylons with the seam up the back. We must be headed someplace that would be cold and where you had to dress up, as well as going to the Mountaineer's Café, which was not cold or fancy.

I added it all up and looked at my bare legs and toes, in horror. "Are we going to church?" They would not let me inside church dressed like this, and I would have to stay in the car all by myself. Church lasted for hours and hours and hours, and I would be all alone outside in the parking lot for the whole service. Plenty of time for a bad man to come up to the car and get me. He would pretend to be nice but would then pull me out of the car and take me away even if I screamed.

"No, we're just going to the Mountaineer's. It's Friday, not Sunday, silly girl!" She patted my leg, then let out a deep sigh and continued tapping her fingers on the steering wheel, but a little more softly.

"Then why are you dressed up?" Maybe she was trying to trick me. Kids at school sometimes did that to me. It had taken me a while to stop believing everything Davey D. said. "And why are you wearing a sweater? Aren't you hot?"

"A little. But it seemed like the right thing to wear."

I noticed there was a bit of sweat on her upper lip, and decided not to ask any more questions. My panic about the church kidnapper slowly died away as I watched the town go by. Kids rode bikes and hollered back and forth at each other. An old lady tottered slowly along on the sidewalk, holding a brown paper grocery bag and tugging back a little dog on a leash that wanted to move much faster. Someday we would get a dog. It would have long, white fur. I would name it Pinky and it would sleep in my bed with me.

Mom seemed to be thinking about other stuff, so I kept my mouth shut for the rest of the ride in case she was in a bad mood. I could do that better than Kevin or Trudy, and it meant I hardly ever got yelled at. Even though they were older, they hadn't figured that out.

Once we got downtown, there were cars everywhere and lots of shoppers going in and out of Penney's and Woolworth's, so we had to park a whole block away from the Mountaineer's Café. When we got to the entrance, I admired the big window that always had mountains and the Mountaineer painted on it. Because it was summertime, there were lots of birds and butterflies and flowers around the mountains, and the Mountaineer wore a straw hat with fringe all around and carried a bucket full of strawberries. The window always looked the best at Christmas with the Mountaineer wearing a Santa hat, a deer that had a red nose, and a red and white striped North Pole.

Mom pulled open the door and I skipped inside. It always smelled like someone was frying bacon and smoking. There were booths made of cracked green vinyl along the front window, but only one of them had customers in it. There were also several Formica-top tables that had round metal chairs with green vinyl seats. Even the walls were light green. But the best seat was at the counter with the tall stools that spun. You could sit right there and watch the waitress get sodas and water and see through a little window into the kitchen where the cook wore a big white hat sort of like the Pope.

"Is the old goat in his office?" Mom asked Sharon, the waitress at the counter. Sharon tilted her head towards the back of the restaurant, and then she and Mom whispered together so low that I couldn't hear.

"Is there a billy goat back there?" I asked, not quite sure whether I was excited or afraid. In cartoons they always butted people and sent them flying through the air and crashing to the ground.

"Yes, but not the kind you're thinking of, kiddo." Sharon patted Mom's shoulders. "Strength, honey," she said to Mom, who headed into the back room. "Now you, little one, hop up here and keep me company."

I climbed onto the stool at the end of the counter and spun around a few times. My feet still couldn't reach the foot rest.

"What'll it be today, kiddo? Chocolate malt? Spaghetti and meatballs?" Sharon was my favorite. I liked her red hair piled high on top of her head, and she called me kiddo just like Daddy used to.

"Spaghetti, please," I said, twisting back and forth on the stool.

"Coming right up." Sharon wrote on a small slip of paper, clipped it onto the order wheel and hollered back into the kitchen, "Al! Kids' spaghetti!"

While I waited, I leaned to the side so that I could see down the hall and into the back room. It was a really big room with lots of old men playing cards at round tables. The front section of the café was almost never crowded, but that back room seemed to be packed no matter what. The men all had several drink glasses in front of them, some empty, some full of what looked to be ginger ale. A few men smoked cigarettes, but most of them were smoking cigars. I didn't know what game they were playing, but I never heard anyone say "Go Fish" or "War." What game didn't include yelling at, or at least talking to each other? I was pretty sure I could figure out what game it was if I could get a look at their cards.

I asked Sharon every time if I could go back there and always got the same answer, a big, fat "No." So I didn't even bother asking this time. I kept watch from afar, but it was boring because everyone just kept staring at their cards, not saying a word, maybe even asleep. Suddenly the oldest man there pulled all the cards from everyone at his table into a pile, neatened them into a deck, and then shuffled them, making the cards into an arch before they went down again. I <u>had</u> to learn how to do that.

Sharon loaded a bunch of plates onto one arm and took them out to the front booth. I quickly slid off the stool and tiptoed toward the back room while she chatted with her customers.

I headed toward the old man who did the fancy shuffling. He saw me and nodded for me to come closer. When I got next to him, he winked at me and then leaned back in his chair, tilted his head up, and puffed out a huge smoke ring. It rose in the air, got wider, and then slowly disappeared. Trails of smoke from many other cigars wisped upward and were broken up by the blades of slow moving ceiling fans.

"Wow," I whispered. I'd never seen anyone do that, not even Aunt Shirley, who smoked a lot.

"Lindy!"

I whipped around to see Sharon standing in the room's doorway, hands on her hips. I ran past her and climbed as fast as I could back onto the stool. Sharon plopped a glass of water in front of me. "You know you're not supposed to go back there."

"Oh, I forgot," I said, feeling my face get hot with the lie.

A plate clattered and Al called, "Order up for the kid!" through the opening from the kitchen and waved at me. Sharon set the spaghetti in front of me and I started in on the feast.

"Why does it take Mom so long to get her pay?" I asked, carefully trying to load a noodle onto my fork.

"It just does." Sharon sounded a little angry, so I went back to keeping quiet. She turned away and began running water in the sink until it was full of suds. Soda glasses and long spoons clinked as she began washing them.

I gave up on the noodles temporarily and decided to work on the meatballs instead. They were my favorite part because we didn't have meat all that often at home. I took a huge bite, then leaned to the side as I chewed, checking on the card games. Mom came around the corner, heading down the hall toward me, blocking my view of the back room. She walked very fast and her face was red and her sweater looked a bit mussed. She held up a bunch of five and ten dollar bills like it was a hand of cards. "We can go now, Lindy."

"But I just got my spaghetti!" I protested, talking with my mouth full of meatball.

Sharon motioned with soapy hands to the stool next to me. "Come over here, Patty." That was my mom's name that other people called her. "Sit, have some coffee and calm down while Lindy eats." Sharon rinsed her hands and wiped them dry on her apron, then filled a cup with dark, thick coffee and set it in

13

front of Mom. I finished my meatballs and concentrated on my noodles once again, which continually slid off my fork. I wanted to eat them like grownups did without having to cut them into small pieces.

Mom sprinkled sugar from the glass pourer into her coffee, stirred it for a bit, and rested her forehead on her hand. "It's just so degrading," she said softly.

"I know," Sharon said. "But he's the boss." She went back to washing dishes.

I went back to watching the card room. It never changed. It seemed like the same men were there every time, with the same drink glasses, and the same cigars and cigarettes. None of them seemed to be having any fun, not even the man who shuffled and blew smoke rings. I had made some progress on my spaghetti noodles and my shirt was still clean. "What's 'degrading' mean?"

Sharon stopped washing and turned toward me, and Mom lifted her head. They both just stared at me for a few seconds. Then Mom smiled a little. "It means I have to find a way to get a better job. And it means you have to study hard in school, so that you will <u>never</u> know what it means."

None of that made sense to me. Grownups were always saying crazy stuff, but I wouldn't dare tell them so.

Mom straightened up in her seat. "Maybe I need to study hard, too." She sipped her coffee and began tapping her fingers against the cup. "I've always wanted to get my degree. I may finally have the motivation to get through all four years. I suppose I should thank the old goat for that."

"Oh, hell no, you should not thank him," Sharon said, and they both laughed.

I held my breath and waited for Mom to scold Sharon for using the Devil's Place word. But Mom didn't even seem to notice, let alone tell her to apologize. And there was that billy goat again. I checked the hallway to make sure it wasn't coming for me.

"How do you do it?" Mom asked Sharon. "How do you keep working here?"

Sharon sighed and wiped her hands on her apron. "He doesn't bother with me anymore, I'm too old. But if he ever crosses the line with any of you younger ones, he'll have hell to pay."

I choked a little on some noodles when I heard the h-word again.

"You okay, honey?" Mom patted my back a few times, then finished her coffee and waved Sharon away when she tried to refill the cup. "If he ever crosses the line," Mom said. She shook her head and sighed. "He always crosses the line. Or maybe I don't even know where the line is anymore." She stepped down from the stool. "Come on Lindy, let's get home. Thanks, Sharon."

We said good bye and headed back to the car. A few cars drove by on either side of the street as we walked. The lane markings were bright, as if they'd just been painted glowing white, a bright line as far as I could see, right down the middle of the street. "Is that it, Mom?"

"Is what it? What are you talking about?"

"The line you and Sharon were talking about. The line that people aren't supposed to cross. If cars go over that line in the middle of the road, there might be a crash and someone might get hurt. So they should never cross that line. Is that what you meant?"

Mom stopped walking and knelt down in front of me on the sidewalk. "You're a very good listener, aren't you? I forget that sometimes." She smoothed my hair with her fingers, kissed my forehead and stood up. "You will never have to worry about anyone crossing that line. I promise you."

I was more confused than I had been before I started asking questions. But I was full of spaghetti and meatballs and looking forward to climbing our tree. Mom put her arm around my shoulders, pulled me close to her, and we walked the rest of the way to the car in silence.

THE END

Joanne M. Kuhns

 Joanne Kuhns grew up in Bellingham, Washington and is currently working on a novel inspired by her childhood. At various times and universities, she studied music, math, business administration, commercial fiction writing and digital forensics, resulting in a couple degrees and certificates. She is a joyfully retired systems engineer and has been a member of the Really Cool Writing Group for more than two decades. Joanne lives in Renton, Washington where she enjoys knitting on her front porch each morning while sipping freshly brewed espresso, watching all her neighbors head to work.

Paddy's Tonsorial Emporium
By Ronald C. Milburn

For thirty years the candy-cane colored barber pole turned outside Paddy's Tonsorial Emporium. Paddy loved the name and claimed it was a great conversation starter with new customers. Through the glass store-front, passing gawkers saw patrons in brown vinyl chairs with chrome handles enjoying their wait. Paddy called the waiting area the liar's section. A plaque on the wall proclaimed, "Only two lies and one fib per customer, please." A bell above the door announced the arriving and departing clients. It was 1967 and Paddy's was the place to be.

Rarely did men enter expecting express service. Skipping the conversation would be akin to gulping champagne rather than sipping it. In fact, Paddy ushered the infrequent mother with a shaggy boy in tow to the front of the line without a single complaint. Had he been with his father, he'd have steeped a while in the tobacco smoke to witness the testosterone ritual.

The shop had two barbers but three chairs. One seat had been unoccupied since the long-hair fad known as the British invasion had come to our shore. Talkative college students no longer arrived in packs, interrupting the old men's conversations, and the high school boys stalled between trims if their parents didn't notice. But the town elders and businessmen still frequented their favorite Saturday morning hangout. The coaches and ballplayers wore flat tops or crew cuts, which required regular maintenance, too.

The owner of the establishment was Patrick Rardin, but everyone called him Paddy. He was the son of Irish immigrants named O'Rardin who 'Americanized' their name at Ellis Island. He was small in stature but had quite a presence. The barber compensated for his short height with over-sized hand gestures and a booming voice. His effervescent personality was contagious, and he'd often invite a customer to his chair with a low dramatic bow and an exaggerated old English accent.

"Come ye vagabond and sit on the throne whilst I relieve you of your heavy burden."

Once seated, he'd wave the smock like a Matador agitating a bull then allow the satin to settle on his entertained guest. He treated everyone as if they were the reason he opened his shop in the morning.

Paddy seldom needed instructions because he knew most scalps, nor did he style hair — styling was for women he insisted. At the barbershop, a whiskery man may ask for a shave, something not available in a beauty parlor. Those patrons reclined while Paddy pressed a piping-hot towel over the stubble. While the facial bristles swelled and softened, Paddy, with abundant flair, sharpened the straight razor on a black leather strap which hung from his chair. He'd dance for our amusement to the rhythm of the slapping blade.

Once the relaxed client was lobster-red, Paddy whipped the shaving cream with a badger brush. After years of experience, he could foam a face without splashing soap in an eye. Then with long smooth strokes, his skilled, unfaltering hand removed the lather. A stinging slap of aftershave announced completion.

When a patron exited, I'd drop from my stool, which faced Paddy's and sweep the floor. It allowed him a moment to draw on his ever-smoldering cigarette. I was thirteen years old working for tips as a shoeshine boy and eager to please my boss. I inherited the job when my older brother enlisted in the marines.

Sometimes, at noon, Paddy sent me for lunch. Across the street, Snappy Fast served hamburgers, fries, and cokes. Patrons at the counter observed the fry-cook prepare paper thin burgers on a buttered, toasted bun.

When I returned with the white bag, the smell of onions couldn't dominate the smoky odor. Since the barbers and most customers smoked cigarettes or cigars, the barbershop was smokier than fall during the leaf-burning season. The occasional sweet fragrance of a pipe added a floral scent to the tobacco cloud.

One and all talked and laughed, paying no attention to the smog. The men discussed sports, complained about their employers, or debated politics, but the most common conversation was Vietnam, where a thousand American soldiers died each month.

Mack Justice, who served in Europe in the second World War, said, "If Ike were in charge the fighting would be over by now."

Willard Tinsman, whose service was in the Pacific, retorted "We need a brilliant general like MacArthur. He chased the Japs out of the palm trees."

World War II had ended twenty-two years prior, but memories remained garden-fresh and opinions hadn't mellowed. Most adults were veterans of overseas conflicts. Paddy was a soldier in the North Africa campaign against Rommel's Panzer tanks.

The other barber was as tall as Paddy was short, so his friends nicknamed him Stretch. He had battled in the Philippines in fierce hand-to-hand combat. Stretch harbored profound, bitter emotions, and he didn't mind expressing his views.

"We fought them in the jungles and beat them."

Stretch had been a sniper, he said he preferred to kill adversaries who slipped away to relieve themselves in private. While they squatted a short distance from their platoon, Stretch took cool-headed aim and squeezed the trigger. Once he delivered the fatal blow, his unsuspecting victim slumped over dead with his pants around his ankles. Then, he'd remove the timepiece from the wrist of the cooling soldier before disappearing into the jungle. Once I challenged him, "You're making that up, Stretch."

Although he didn't respond, the next Saturday, he called out my name as I entered.

"George."

"What?"

"Look in my drawer."

While nosey rubberneckers in the liars' section took it in, I pulled the knob.

"Pull out that velvet bag with the gold drawstrings."

I obeyed, but Stretch refused to accept the sack as I attempted to hand it to him.

"Open it."

I loosened the drawstring and widened the opening. Dozens of wristwatches lay tangled inside the pouch. Dumbstruck, I looked into Stretch's intense eyes, which assured me his stories were true.

"I earned each one in there."

Breaking from his piercing stare, I again investigated the contents. It was eerie to think Stretch had removed them from dead men he had killed himself.

He said, "Those Vietcong are the same. Just shoot, stab, or burn them until wiped out. They're not human."

It disturbed me to listen to such talk because I had Japanese classmates whose fathers taught at the University, and they were good kids. Though our country's former enemies were now on agreeable terms, many an ex-soldier still harbored an intense hatred.

Provoked by Stretch's tirade, a young man with long curls and a beard looked up from the magazine he wasn't reading. He seemed unable to hold his tongue any longer.

"It's not the same."

"What?" Stretch asked.

"Vietnam isn't the Philippines, .it isn't an island. The North Vietnamese run into Laos, and President Johnson won't let the American soldiers follow them."

"So?"

"So, it's just another reason it's a dumb war."

Angry eyes focused on the argumentative man while a few heads dropped lower into their magazine to avoid the oncoming conflict. Until he continued, I could have heard a pin drop.

"This war is stupid."

Stretch pointed his scissors with sniper accuracy at the heretic. A hippy infiltrated this sanctuary of unanimous opinion.

Stretch shouted, "You're just afraid to fight for your country. You're chicken like Cassius Clay."

The intruder replied, "Well, I am like Mohammed Ali in one way. I'm not antiwar. I'm anti-this-war. This war is unwinnable the way it's being fought."

"Bull, you can't choose your wars. When America calls, you answer."

Paddy intervened and touched Stretch's shoulder.

"We don't argue with customers."

Stretch returned to his chair and continued with a less quarrelsome tone.

"We'll win in Vietnam."

The student replied, "Like we did in Korea?"

A crimson glow crept up Stretch's neck and face as he stepped away from his chair, again. Glad I had a good seat for the bout, I awaited Stretch's retort.

"We'll win in Vietnam."

He pulled on his beard, appearing circumspect before responding to Stretch's claim.

"Stretch, do you read the Bible?"

"Yes, well, sometimes."

"There's a passage in First Kings. It says, 'Don't brag while putting on your armor like a man who is removing his.'"

I didn't understand, and from Stretch's furrowed brow, he didn't either. The college student rose and headed toward the door without a haircut. But as he left, he explained the scripture.

"It means, brag after you win the war. Everything else is just trash talk."

After the hippy left, Stretch returned to an unclipped sideburn. There was a lack of conversation for an introspective moment.

Stretch said, "I'll admit, it's a heck of a way to win a war. If you go to fight, go to win."

Mr. Lannon, a man my father's age, jumped up and headed toward me.

Mr. Lannon said, "We can agree on that."

I dropped from my perch atop my shoeshine chair, and Mr. Lannon climbed up to take my place. He wore brown cowboy boots and asked me to shine them every Saturday.

He said, "Son, use black polish, and they'll turn black in time."

I rolled up his cuffs and applied the shoe cream as he settled on my stool. Though I polished and buffed the leather, it never changed color. Mr. Lannon had fought the Germans at Normandy in World War II, where he left a lung and two feet of small intestine. He claimed he saw the smoke puff from the rifle that shot him. When the bullet ripped through his jacket, it ignited a glove, the fire cauterized the wound and may have saved his life.

"Hedgerows," he blurted.

I tried to shine his moving boots, but it was impossible.

"Those blasted trees and dirt banks provided perfect cover for the enemy. The Nazis picked us off as we approached on those narrow lanes." Excited, he kicked, causing me to smear his pants. "They ambushed us like in Vietnam." His bellowing, stomping, and shifting made both barbers stop shearing. But in a while, he placed his boot back on my stand. "You've got to keep pushing because an army can't win without taking ground. Westmoreland won't defeat the North Vietnamese by killing more of them than us."

Several in the audience nodded their agreement. Pointing at no one in particular, Mr. Lannon waved his finger and continued his rant while increasing his volume.

"That's what Patton told us. 'When you're scared, drive forward. Keep going until you grease your tank tracks with their guts,' and we did. We drove those Jerrys to Berlin."

When he flung his arms, cigarette ashes fell in my hair. I chased his boots around my stand while trying to brush away hot ash. With his rant at a crescendo, he thundered, "You can't win a war without taking the land." Mr. Lannon leaned back and stared at me, "I don't have all day, boy."

Once finished, I hoped he wouldn't notice the polish on his pants. A few months later, doctors diagnosed Mr. Lannon with lung cancer. Since he only had one lung, the surgeon didn't operate. Treatments weren't successful, and he knew his fate. I visited him in the hospital. Though he was frail, and his mind foggy from the medication, he remembered me.

"Hey, shoeshine boy, what are you doing here?"

"I came to see if those boots are black."

"Nope, they're still brown."

He pointed to the closet, "Look in there; see for yourself."

As Mr. Lannon raised his head from the pillow, I opened the cabinet door.

I said, "I should have dyed them a long time ago. Do you mind if I take the boots home and fix them?"

Exhausted, he dropped his head.

"That'll be great, son."

Then he drifted to sleep, and his wife nodded her approval. I applied dye twice then gave them a spit shine. Before morning, Mr. Lannon died. If not for his war injury, he may have survived. He was a delayed casualty from the Normandy invasion. They buried him in his black boots.

Back at Paddy's, the bell clanged, and I turned as Toby's girlfriend rolled his wheelchair into the barbershop.

Toby said, "Hi, everybody."

Everyone responded in kind.

"Hi, Toby."

"I'll be done soon," Stretch announced.

As Stretch wiped the hair from his customer with a powdered brush, the man ran his index finger around the inside of his collar.

"I'll be right with you."

"No hurry," Toby said.

As the itchy patron paid, he pawed at his neck like a mutt chasing a flea. After he left, Stretch swept the floor and pointed to a spot beside his chair.

"You're next, Toby."

No one complained when Stretch didn't make Toby wait. He'd been cutting Toby's hair since his return from Vietnam. Still keeping his military haircut required regular appointments. On earlier visits, Toby sat in his wheelchair while Stretch bent to shorten his hair.

Toby said, "Not this time."

His childhood sweetheart pushed the wheelchair forward.

"I'll sit in the barber chair," he exclaimed, "I've got new legs, and I need to practice walking."

Toby surprised everyone as he stood. He took two steps, then wrestled, stepped, and twisted into the chair. His brunette fiancé's cloud-nine smile lit the room.

"Wonderful," Paddy said.

"That's amazing," said Stretch. "How long have you had those?"

"Just three weeks. I've practiced until my stubs are sore, but I wanted to get back on two feet — even if they are plastic."

"Good for you," Stretch said.

"I know it's been hard to cut my hair with me sitting in a wheelchair."

Stretch patted his friend on the shoulder as he pumped the chair higher.

Paddy said, "Next victim, please."

A distinguished gentleman extinguished his cigar in a hefty chrome ashtray, and with both hands on his cane, pushed himself erect. The eminent citizen wore a handsome suit with a fresh red carnation in the lapel. He removed the jacket and hung it on a hook beside his expensive fedora. As he shuffled toward Paddy, I noticed his brilliant, white shirt. Though it was summer, he had long sleeves. Gold cufflinks with ebony stones adorned his starched and pressed French cuffs.

Once seated, Paddy wrapped the dark cape over the silver-haired businessman's shoulders.

"How are you today, Doc?"

"I'm doing just fine, thank you."

Though not a real doctor, he was a medic in World War One. So, the troops called him Doc, and it stuck. In my youth, many men went by a rank they earned in the war. A former Sergeant was Sarge.

Chief was a name for a Chief Petty Officer, and Gunny had been a Gunnery Sergeant. If someone achieved the rank of Colonel, he was Colonel the rest of his life.

Doc owned the funeral home in our town. Though his boys ran the business after he retired, he stopped by the office every day for an hour or two. The crisp crease in the pants appeared sharp enough to cut steel. On a typical day, Doc was quiet, but on that day, he spoke uncoerced.

"I received terrible news today, Paddy."

The buzzing of multiple chitchats ceased. The mortician had buried a relative for most people there, so he was familiar with sad news or even shocking news. But, terrible news made heads turn.

"The army called," He paused for dramatic effect then continued, "Billy Branch died in Vietnam. They're shipping his body home."

Disbelief hung thicker than the cigarette smoke.

"What did he say?" someone whispered.

"Billy Branch died?"

Silence interrupted conversations as we tried to absorb the news. Old men shook their heads, and young adults appeared unable to move as they stared into nothingness. Billy was the first Vietnam war fatality from our little town, and most people knew him. He'd been a basketball star in high school and held several records.

Paddy dropped his eyes and seemed too shocked to continue. Scissors drooped from inactive fingers. The older barber broke the silence.

"Tell me it's not so. Billy was such a nice boy from a good family. I've known him since he was a baby. I gave him his first haircut while his father took pictures, and his mother entertained him. He only cried a little..."

Doc interrupted, "The army is sending an escort with his body."

"That's good," Stretch said.

Paddy lifted the ten-pound scissors and struggled to trim Doc's hair.

"How?"

"Don't know," Doc replied. "But we can open the casket."

"Well, that's a consolation....I mean, for his mother's sake," Paddy said.

The mortician nodded, raised his silver eyebrows, and sighed, "It helps a mother to see her boy and say goodbye."

A man wearing a VFW hat asked, "Does the family want a military service?"

"Yes."

"I'll tell the members, so they can prepare."

The veteran lit a cigarette, what else could he do? He inhaled then exhaled the smoke, adding to the ever-present haze.

"We'll give him a fine send off....an honor guard. We won't be short of volunteers, that's for sure. The VFW and the American Legion will be there."

Toby sighed, "Marsha and I'll be there."

"Gosh, I hope he didn't suffer," someone muttered.

For a while, the only sound was scissors. As clippings settled onto the satin capes, waiting customers stared at magazines without turning pages. No need, they weren't reading. I suppose some men remembered Billy on the basketball court, while others stared into the battlefields of their memories, wondering why boys such as Billy died, and they came home.

Paddy changed the topic.

"How's the foot, Doc?"

"Worse than usual. I think we're in for a change in the weather. But those missing toes are throbbing."

"Toes?" Paddy asked. "I don't remember how you lost them. You'd better tell me again,"

Doc had told the story many times, but Paddy wanted someone to stop the painful silence.

"It happened in the war," Doc said.

He projected his voice so the willing spectators could listen to his repeat performance. His introduction, for the adults, was akin to, "once upon a time" in my childhood fairy tales.

"I spent 1917 and 1918 in a freezing, wet trench in France. The Germans were dug-in fifty yards from us; we could see them. For months we were in those trenches, shooting and being shot." Doc directed his attention to me because I hadn't heard his story. From atop my perch on my shoeshine stool, I listened.

"On a fateful winter morning in early 1918, word came to attack. On signal, we crawled out and ran toward the enemy. Since I was a medic, I had a satchel of medical supplies instead of a rifle.

I'd gone ten yards when the first man fell, so I wrapped gauze around his head, it stopped the bleeding, and an aide helped him back to our line. The fighting was brutal but lasted just a short time. The assault was a failure, as usual. Our troops retreated, but I stayed behind to treat the injured."

Paddy spun Doc toward the mirror for approval, then turned him back to face me.

He continued, "The enemy didn't shoot our medics, and we avoided shooting theirs. But I was carrying a wounded soldier, and a bullet ripped into my leg. Before I fell, another went through the soldier and then through my shoulder. I dropped into a shallow ditch and tried not to scream. Once over the initial shock, I reached for morphine. After an injection, I had minor relief and pushed a bandage into the hole in my shoulder before wrapping my bleeding calf. There was nothing I could do for my unconscious patient except plug his wound."

The librarian at story hour didn't have a quieter crowd.

"I didn't move for fear a German might finish me."

"How long did you lie there?" I blurted.

"A day and night, and the next day, too. It was frigid on the battlefield, and I nestled against my patient, so we could share body heat. We faced nose to nose on the frozen ground. He was a young lieutenant with dark hair and brown eyes. As he exhaled, his breath fogged in the winter air. During the second day, his breathing slowed. He died before the sunset."

Doc looked at the ceiling and recollected the scene.

"A few hours later, we got stormy weather, and the clouds covered the moon. It was darker than dark, so I hoped to move. I gave myself more morphine and lifted myself from the ditch. Through snow and mud, with excruciating pain, I pulled with my good arm and pushed with my uninjured leg. I made it to our line, and someone yanked me to safety. I don't remember being carried to a field hospital, but by the time we arrived, I regained consciousness. The foot on my injured leg was black from poor circulation and frostbite. When the orderlies removed my boot, three toes fell off….I didn't feel it."

Paddy brushed Doc's neck and pulled off the cape. The undertaker leaned forward and directed his next comment to me.

"I left toes in France, young man, but my head thinks they're still there. The pain is a reminder of my patient whose body heat kept me alive. When severe weather approaches, my foot throbs. In my dreams, the phantom digits ache, and the dead lieutenant visits me. Even though it's been fifty years, I can't forget him. I suppose I never will."

Silence followed the undertaker who limped toward the door. He retrieved his suit jacket from a hook, but before buttoning it, he removed a cigar. He held our attention as he lit it then put on his hat. As he pulled on the doorknob, he turned and scanned his mesmerized audience.

He said, "Won't be any frostbite in Vietnam. But it'll be hell."

The bell tinkled as he departed. Stretch finished Toby's haircut, then the old men viewed as he maneuvered into his wheelchair. His girlfriend pushed him, and an entering patron held the door open.

"Thanks," Toby said.

"Sure, anytime."

After Toby passed, the new arrival looked puzzled as he surveyed the room.

"This place is quiet, did somebody die?"

The somber crowd ignored his question, a common quip. To avoid the topic, Paddy jumped in the air and clicked his heels, imitating a leprechaun.

He asked, "Who amongst you with ten toes wants a haircut?"

His next victim hustled from his seat and hurried forward.

Paddy asked, "Are you a Cubs fan or a Cardinal?"

As he placed the apron around his patron's neck, I slumped on my stool and pondered the gravity of war. On other Saturdays, I'd listened to veterans recount their stories of valor. But now Billy was dead, Toby had no legs, and it was real. I realized then, atop my shoeshine stool, not everyone returned home with exciting tales. My brother was on the other side of the world in Vietnam, and I feared I'd never see him whole, or worse, alive again.

I tried to shake off my right-of-passage moment, but I never regained my blissful innocence. Mom put ignored cap-rifles and plastic army helmets in the attic. She tossed them one spring-cleaning day while I was at the post office enrolling in the selective service.

The summer before college, on Saturdays, I strolled to the barbershop for a haircut and a shoeshine. From atop the stand, I'd eavesdrop on the veterans while pretending to watch the teen buff my shoes. As I sat on my draft card, I wondered if the boy had yet gleaned what I had learned five summers ago. If not, he'd learn the damaged men who recounted their war stories weren't bragging. They were sharing. It was therapy offered nine-to-five at Paddy's Tonsorial Emporium.

Ronald C. Milburn

Ronald Milburn lives in Clermont, Florida with his wife, Susan. He was born in Charleston, Illinois where he graduated from Eastern Illinois with a B.A. in psychology. He lived for many years in Illinois and Indiana, where he raised his four children. Ronald is a retired minister and building contractor.

Now Would be Forever
By David Tarpenning

When Henry Stevens stood alone on the ridge surveying the rich, black fields below, something he couldn't describe nor explain began in his heart and spread over and around him. A feeling inspired by the music of wind through the trees or perhaps something internal-- the defense he had built over the years to preserve and protect this land his grandfather homesteaded-- land his father later passed to him.

Years ago, when all that he assumed to be permanent was about to be swept away by the Great Depression, he did not break. Jaw set, fire in his eyes, Henry told himself, *"You must do the things you think you cannot do. You must...if you intend to save all that you hold dear."*

So he did. He worked at the cannery in town during the day, coming home at night to plow, to plant, or to harvest until midnight; perhaps until dawn when he would milk their one cow by lantern-light before returning to the cannery, exhausted. His wife would churn the rich cream into butter she sold to neighbors who could afford it, given free to those who could not.

As light follows dark---as when the sun finishes warming the other side of Earth and returns---the Depression receded into history. People could breathe again. Smiles returned to faces that had been pinched by hunger and doubt. Though food was again on tables, people were wary. Lessons learned through those troubled years taught them that ease was earned through hard work and that time alone could not be trusted.

Too many years of trials and tribulations had marked Henry. They manifested themselves in the slump of his shoulders. The feeling he could neither describe nor explain was responsible for deep sadness around his eyes. Each day now, he searched the distant county road for a lone traveler, backpack across his shoulders. If he were there, the traveler, looking up, would wave as he turned into the lane leading to the farmhouse on the ridge.

If he were there. Perhaps someday.

•••

It had been unspoken between them, a simple acknowledgment. Because Henry was rough around the edges he did not declare it to be *love* as it's commonly known. He was shy, too, which complicated matters and made the acknowledgment even more difficult. Urged on by everyone in the town or simply deciding for himself that he had the courage to ask Matilda Adams to marry him, he did.

They were united one summer Saturday in the small brown log church between the county road and the unruly river. They celebrated with friends at the small cafe in town, toasting with iced tea, eating from a lopsided wedding cake baked by Simon Evans who owned the cafe. There would be no wedding trip--no escape to anywhere. There was work to be done. Work until each night they fell dead from it or until the very real threat of losing everything passed.

One day, with almost no fanfare, the Depression slowed, stopped, but not without leaving human casualties in its wake---thousands of folks who lost everything including their land. Henry and Matilda survived. The land they loved remained in the family. Someday it would be in the hands of their children---three as different from each other as night from day.

Phillip was the first born. At the end of his baptism at age seven, he came up from the river smiling, wiping the water from his eyes, blessed by the Reverend Clyde Newcomb. He was inquisitive, articulate and amiable--his parents were thankful for the grace they had been given.

Two years later, they gave thanks for Rebekah, born when Phillip was nine. His sister was also inquisitive, articulate, amiable---and determined. One might even have said stubborn. That *one* would have been her father! Almost from the time she could speak, she vowed she could--and would--do whatever she wanted with her life.

Phillip graduated from college with a degree in construction engineering, married and moved to a city nearby to pursue his career. A year after Phillip married, Henry William

Stevens was born. Two years later, he and his wife were blessed with John Matthew Stevens.

Determination shaped Rebekah's life. She would, she said with absolute certainty, become a doctor. It was unheard of at that time for women to pursue a career in medicine because the path was purposely littered with obstacles created to discourage them. Roadblocks thrown in the way by male practitioners who, firm in their conviction, agreed with one another that a woman doctor would be inferior. Frustrated, weary with having to fight to achieve her dream, she admitted to Henry one evening that she had decided to stop fighting.

He shook his head and took her hands in his. Bringing up from his past the same words he had used to encourage himself, he admonished his daughter, *"Rebekah, you must do the things you think you cannot do. You must...if you intend to save all that you hold dear."* A new fire was ignited, she achieved what had appeared to be impossible-- Rebekah Stevens, *MD.*

And finally, there was Isaac, the youngest, the son his mother described as a *'sweet boy at loose ends'*. A loving child who became a thoughtful and kind young man, it was his nature to be more aware of things around him than on what he needed to do to make his way in the world. He was blissfully indifferent to what attitudes he should have, what strengths he should use to prepare himself for life. There were times when his father was afraid Isaac's gentle nature might someday be troublesome.

For example, Isaac appeared one afternoon on the ridge leading a horse. He had witnessed something unacceptable--a man mistreating the animal. He offered the abuser all he had-- five wadded up dollar bills-- and the man accepted. Isaac had no idea what to do with the horse. He only knew his humanity insisted that he save it. And so he did.

Henry frowned and scratched his head. "Son," he said kindly, but with his usual practicality, "it will take a miracle to fatten that poor bag of bones and make him fit to work. You'll have to do double chores to pay for his feed."

Isaac nodded. "Yes, Papa, I know. I don't mind."

Because often at night, Isaac searched the sky from the ridge for his favorite constellation, he named his horse Orion. It wasn't feed or hay alone that put meat on Orion's bones or gave luster to his coat, brightness to his eyes. It was love. Love as simple as Isaac, finishing twice his chores late at night, hugging his horse around the neck, brushing him and whispering in his ear. Responding to Isaac's love, Orion adapted easily to the saddle. The two were a common sight along the county road at dawn each morning.

Where Henry had admonished the first two of his children to "*follow your dreams unfailingly as far as you can*" the most he had for Isaac was "*go out into the world and do good.*" What it lacked in specificity, it made up for in intensity; it was a heavy admonition that puzzled Isaac. There was no how-to, no why. It was a momentous project that came without instructions.

So one summer night, Isaac filled a backpack with a few belongings--he didn't have much yet--and went out alone into the world. The note he left under the pillow on his bed read, *"I will do as you told me, Papa. And I will come back when I can make you proud of me. I love you and Mama with all my heart. Your son, Isaac."*

Devastated, Henry at first blamed himself for sending his son on a fool's errand. But later, when he was not in his truck searching every county road, every gravel path--searching entire villages for his son--he screamed at God. He shouted at an unyielding heaven, threats that he would find a way to get back at God for what He had done to him. And finally, when he was exhausted and desperate, he begged God to tell him, *"Why did you take my son away?"* When there was no answer he threatened, *"Then I will pray to a different god!"*

Matilda, because the God she knew was a jealous God, was afraid their sorrow would be magnified, that it would become even more unbearable. She pleaded with Henry, *"Be calm, my love. Isaac will come up the road, turn into our lane and we will see him again. Perhaps someday soon."*

His face a grim mask, he spat the words, "You don't know that. Stop! That means nothing." Then, beginning to cry, he would ask, "Why don't you cry? I cry because our son is gone.

Not out of sight. Not just away. Isaac is gone. I cry because I cannot touch him or talk with him or laugh with him. I cry because I don't know where he is. If he is safe, if he is fed, if he has a bed at night. Oh, God! I cannot stand this." Frenzied, he circled the kitchen table, smashing his fist into the top until his hand bled. "And you"--he jabbed a bloodied finger at his wife, his voice trembling with rage--"you don't cry. You are his mother, yet you don't feel. Why?"

"Because, Henry, I am afraid to cry. I am afraid to feel even though despair is inside my head and my heart every day. I am afraid to cry because if I do, I am saying that there is no longer hope that perhaps someday Isaac will appear on the road, come up the lane and he will be home."

Her soft reply made him even more angry.

"I don't believe you. You laugh with Philip and Rebekah. With our grandsons. You have feelings. Why can't you cry for our son? Why can't you cry for Isaac?"

She shook her head. The answer she gave did not satisfy him. She had told him simply--she was afraid. He didn't know that every night after he was asleep, Matilda went to Isaac's room, knelt beside his bed clutching the pillow that gave out the familiar scent of their son and prayed. Prayed until her mouth was dry and her throat ached. Until she thought she might die of grief. But she would not give in to tears. She would not give up hope.

The season of new beginnings silently began to blanket the woods and fields below the ridge. Bitterness between Henry and Matilda disappeared in the sunlit mornings; vanished in air that smelled of moist earth and dew-drenched crops. Sunrise came early; brilliant colors painted the eastern sky. Cadres of puffy clouds marched across the horizon. In the river bottoms, morning mist rose and drifted in the air like smoke from a hundred campfires.

As it had always been and probably would be forever, there was work to be done. They plowed and planted. Did chores. When Phillip and his sons came to help, they worked side by side with Matilda and Henry, eating together around the kitchen table at noon. There was so much comfort in that familiar pattern.

Workdays for Henry were exactly that; idle days were meant for talk, walking the fences to see if repairs were needed, brushing Orion. So much of Isaac was in his horse that this simple chore brought Henry closer to his son --wherever he was.

One summer Tuesday, Matilda and Henry sat down at the old kitchen table to a country breakfast.

"What a nice big breakfast for an idle day," he commented, starting first on the biscuits.

"Why, Henry, dear....it's Tuesday, a workday. You always go to the feed store in town on Tuesday."

"Tuesday? Yes, Tuesday. So it is. I suppose I won't be gone long. Just some feed for the cows."

"And remember? Hay for Orion although there's still part of a bale left."

"Oh, yes. I forgot about Orion."

"And tell Claude hello. And hello to his wife."

"Claude? Claude. And--and his wife." It was said with hesitation.

"Claude Summerfield. At the feed store. Evangeline...his wife. Henry, do you feel alright? The feed can wait. We have enough to last until the weekend. We could both go in on Saturday." Frowning, Matilda reached across and put a hand to his forehead. Cool to the touch. There was no fever. "Are you sure you feel well enough to go into town?"

"Of course. I'll just be an hour or two. I still have chores here."

They finished breakfast together. He kissed her on the cheek. She watched--concerned--from the kitchen window as he drove away.

Henry pulled the truck onto the county road going south noting, for no particular reason, that the Addison's mailbox was where it had always been. The Schrader's stone fence lined the barrow ditch on the west. He passed the water tower, the train station. Drove past the feed store. When he reached Libby's Mercantile, he knew he had gone too far. Nothing on either side of him looked familiar. He turned around in the middle of the street heading back north. As he passed the feed store the second time, Claude Summerfield, sweeping the front sidewalk, shouted, "Henry! Stop!"

But there was no acknowledgment that Henry had heard. He didn't stop. Didn't even glance toward the man waving feverishly from the sidewalk.

The railroad divided the town in half. When Henry bounced across the tracks headed north--only then did he realize he had passed the feed store again. Only then did he understand. He was lost. Adrift on a road he had traveled without any problem for decades.

He pulled his battered pick-up into the service station north of the tracks. Using the public telephone, with trembling hands he dialed the only number he could remember. His wife's calm, pleasant *Hello* did nothing to soothe him.

"Tilda," he said, eyes closed, his voice shaking. "Tilda, I'm at the service station in town. I--I-- don't remember how to get home."

For some time, he had forgotten small things: keys, his wallet, meetings. He had forgotten, for days, to feed the cows and Orion. Matilda did it without calling his attention to it. She did it because thirty-seven years ago they made a promise to love and cherish each other, vowing--both of them--it would be "in sickness and in health."

Now, fearful, phone to her ear, she said softly: "Let me talk to one of the service station attendants. I will ask him to bring you home and I'll drive him back to town while you rest. And, Henry dear, don't fret. We'll get through this together just as we always have. I promise. Because I love you."

Without wanting to but knowing they must, they went together to town the next day to see Doc Hutchinson. Henry pale and frightened---Matilda, uncertain. There would be tests. Uncomfortable tests that made Henry feel as though he were a visitor in his own life. The questions threatened him, gave him the sense that something was out of balance, that he had somehow misplaced himself.

At the end of the week, as gently, as kindly as he could, Doc Hutchinson delivered the verdict.

"Yes, the symptoms were real. There will be good days and bad at first," he told them. "The disease is progressive and at this time there is no cure. Nothing medically that can be done."

Henry, having trouble understanding what he heard, stared at the doctor.

"But Henry, this diagnosis does not mean you shouldn't work. You must continue to do the things you are familiar with. Every day store up memories. Hang onto them as long as you can."

Henry and Matilda drove home in silence, knowing their life would never be the same. Aware that everything would be different from this time on.

Phillip and his sons now came more often---their son, dutiful, loving, eager to make his father's life easier, taking time away from his considerable work. And Rebekah, when she could leave the hospital in the city, came to the farm to help her mother with the house and the garden. Working alongside her to prepare the evening meal, then eat together around the kitchen table. Rebekah often reached for her father's hand, would squeeze it gently, smiling at him.

"Rebekah," he would say, sometimes looking into empty space as if there would be a reminder of what he intended to say but couldn't find it.

For the man on the ridge, life had turned on its head. Now, as he surveyed the hills and trees he loved so much, he must commit the scene to memory. Soon memories would be all he'd have---vague, shifting, receding into a dark place within his mind--to be kept for times when the familiar would become the unrecognized. Barely holding off something that raged within him.

Just before sunset one summer day as Henry looked out over the woods and fields, he saw someone on the county road below. It was dusk, the image unclear. But as he stared, his mind told him it was Isaac. Excited, he stumbled to the house shouting,

"Tilda, Isaac is coming up the lane! Come quick...I just saw him on the road."

Wiping her hands on her apron, she rushed out the door, down the steps. Together they waited beside the grove of trees at the end of the lane for Isaac to appear. Waited until the sun fell behind the trees. Until Matilda gently touched his arm.

"Henry," she said softly, "Come in for supper now. Isaac will be coming home. Maybe someday soon, my love." She put an arm around him and led him to the house.

Good days, Henry went about his work with his old enthusiasm. At other times--and there were many--the will to work, to hope, to believe in tomorrow, was pushed away by despair. But whatever the day brought, at the end of it Matilda would find him at the top of the ridge, staring at the distant county road for the lone traveler. And it seemed to Henry that the trees whispered words that promised there could someday be hope-- *the traveler, looking up, would wave as he turned into the lane leading to the farmhouse.*

One afternoon in early fall, when the sun was in no hurry to disappear behind the trees, when all of nature seemed to stop and breathe before dusk colored the west, he *was* there, waving at the man high up on the ridge. But the man, the one with sad eyes and the slump in his shoulders, knowing it was not to be, that bitter disappointment was all there was, all there might ever be, turned--disconsolate -- toward the house.

Perhaps God had heard Henry above the chaos of despair. Perhaps the God whom Matilda feared was not a jealous God but a caring one. But most certainly, it was God who smiled on the man on the ridge that afternoon.

In Henry's path was a young man with a backpack slung across his shoulders. A young man with a familiar face, a familiar smile. "Hello, Papa," he said rushing with open arms to greet his father.

Henry opened his mouth but couldn't speak. His lips trembled. He began to shake. Sobbing, he clutched at Isaac's coat, grabbing handfuls of it, pulling him closer. "Please don't leave us ever again. Oh, Isaac, how we've missed you."

Matilda, in the kitchen preparing dinner, unaccustomed to hearing two voices in the late afternoon, rushed to the door. In the fading light, two men--one who had *lived* much of life, one who had *seen* much of life--embraced. A hand flew to her throat. Lost in the intensity of the moment, she could do no more than whisper *Isaac* over and over again as she ran to him.

Clinging tightly to each other afraid this would be a dream disappearing with the sun, they marched to the house, joy flowing upward through the trees on a bridge of laughter into the star-sprinkled night.

Over supper around the old kitchen table, Isaac told of his journey through the months since he left home. Following his father's instructions, he roamed the world. Where he found

50

anguish and despair, he brought hope. Where he found devastation and deprivation, he brought help. When he left home with his meager belongings, he found work in a soup kitchen in Cincinnati feeding the hungry. From there, he traveled with missionaries to Africa to build a school for children who would otherwise have no education. Task finished, he joined a caravan of tradesmen going to Egypt to help find water in the desert. From there, to Italy to help build a church. And at last, home to the house on the ridge.

Taking his father's hand, looking into his eyes, Isaac said "I have seen a lot. I have witnessed what love and humanity can do. Papa, I hope I did what you asked of me. My journeys are finished. I would like to stay here and work with you and Mama on the farm...if there's room for me."

How could it be so simple, that what they had prayed for through days of anguish and torment when hope was almost gone---how could it now be found in the answer to so simple a request?

"Oh, yes, Isaac!" His tears gathered and overflowed. He stroked his son's cheek. "Oh, my darling boy, yes! Yes."

Through all that had been so wrong --through suffocating sadness, doubt, fear--it was right that holding onto each other never to let go, Henry and Isaac sat at the old kitchen table together.

Quietly, Matilda reached for her coat and pulled it tightly around her. She would visit the ridge tonight under the cold autumn moon to survey the silvered landscape, the fields down to the county road knowing what she would find but driven to assure herself that a miracle had happened. She wanted to see, to feel--and it was just as she knew it would be-- the moonlit ribbon of road, empty. The traveler at last was home.

For the first time in the long days of intolerable despair, she allowed herself to cry, tears running silently down through the lines time had written on her face, all the way to those lines that tonight surrounded a smile.

Perhaps...someday was now and *now* would be forever.

David Tarpenning

When David Tarpenning retired from the University of Oklahoma after 21 years in the classroom, he knew what he wanted to do. He wanted to write. To write something other than lesson plans, text supplements and syllabi. So he joined an online writing community. He read at least a dozen books about writing fiction. He took the advice of established authors wherever he could find it. And he writes-- early morning, late at night---completely happy doing exactly what he wanted to do. He has been published in *Chronicles of the West, Catholic Digest, Columbia Student Press Review, Computer* Bytes and *American Education Journal.* He can be reached through *thewritestuff.live* and *ddtarpenning.com*

Revolt of the Blessed Virgin Mother

By Mary Alice Dixon

I did not want to be the Blessed Virgin Mother. I wanted to be an angel. A singing angel, with gold wings. But Sister Mary Agnes, director of St. A's fifth grade Christmas play, had other ideas.

"You, my child, are no angel," Sister tells me. "Angels sing. You cannot carry a tune. You will be the Blessed Mother. Your role is to be seen, not heard."

I am crushed. Eleven years old. 1962. A small southern town, a small southern school. I am expected to be obedient.

At rehearsal, in St. A's damp December nave, Sister Mary Agnes points at me, commanding, "Look pious, girl, and stay silent."

This is not a role that suits me. No matter what they say, I want to be an angel. But, as instructed, I keep my mouth shut. I mean, you can't talk back to a nun. Can you? Plopping down in a hard wooden pew at rehearsal, I tug at the itchy wool skirt of my Catholic

School uniform, look around the 1950s Southern Gothic church where our play will be performed and study my classmates.

Every other girl in my fifth grade class is cast as an angel, a singing angel. With halos of sparkly silver Christmas tree tinsel. Looking like little princesses. On the night of the play, they will wear bright heavenly wings made from coat hangers, tissue paper, and gold glitter. Wings made as Bible Study homework during the first week of Advent. Their mothers helped them craft their costumes. I know, because one of the angels, my best friend Patty Ann, told me.

"Really," my mother says, in a moment of a candor, "I hardly think making coat hanger wings should count as Bible Study." Standing at our avocado-colored kitchen counter, she wipes her hands on her polka dot apron and hugs me.

Of course, there will also be singing shepherds. Picked from the rowdiest of fifth grade boys. And listen to this, these kids get to wear play clothes – cowboy shirts with dungarees like they're Roy Rogers.

How about the three Wise Men? Those guys are gussied up like little priests, no doubt Sister Mary Agnes's ultimate goal, what with their fancy hiked-up purple vestments lent by Father Frank.

Every single kid in my class gets to speak or sing but me. Even my nemesis, smart-aleck Joey Patrick Purcelli, cast, unsuitably, as the good St. Joseph, has a speaking part. How can this be? I always considered St. Joseph to be no more than the Blessed Mother's sidekick. But, oh no, this Joseph shouts out to imaginary innkeepers, waving his grandpa's hickory cane like he's Captain Hook with a sword. Worse, old Joey P. will wear his father's nasty brown bathrobe, a Mile too long, smelling of Vicks vapor rub and Smith Brothers cherry cough drops. And what's with the towering red and white headpiece Joey's mother made him from a striped cotton tablecloth? It looks the Cat in the Hat landed on that boy's head. No wonder Joseph can't get anybody a room at the inn.

But don't feel sorry for Joseph because he gets to speak while the Blessed Mother of God just walks quietly behind him, pretending to be holy. She, the Mother of God, in a white granny nightgown. With huge pockets. Where did they find this thing? On a dead nun?

"This," I say to my own blessed mother, "this, is not fair."

My mother sighs.

I continue to complain. To anyone who will listen, and everyone who won't, including Sister Mary Agnes. To no avail.

Sister tells me not only can I not sing, I have a bad attitude.

It looks like I am stuck in my role.

At every rehearsal Sister reminds me I better be quiet and look where I'm going. Just carry Baby Jesus down the church aisle, place him in the manger, then kneel, hands folded in prayer.

For the whole rest of the Christmas play.

Come on. That's it for the Mother of God?

And, get this, my fake Baby Jesus is a fat little apparition in hard plaster, on loan from a wall niche in my family's oak-paneled living room.

Yes, Sister tells me, Baby Jesus is played by my very own parents' hand-painted eighteen-inch Infant of Prague statue, his red velvet Czechoslovakian robes partially concealed by a cloth diaper with safety pins and my little brother Michael's baby blue, lace-edged christening blanket.

"Somebody," I whisper to Patty Ann during the last rehearsal, "needs to put a stop to this."

"Quiet," Sister Mary Agnes commands me. "How many times do I have to tell you, child, the Blessed Virgin Mother's role is to be seen and not heard?"

Sister looks at me hard, her black eyes unblinking behind round wire-rimmed bifocals.

I lower my head.

#

When the big night arrives, my fifth grade class gathers in the church vestibule, costumed and ready. The angels have their wings. The Wise Men stand tall in Father Frank's royal purple vestments. The shepherds, ready to rumble, carry cut-out cardboard sheep that look like deformed dinosaurs. Saint Joseph plays around pretending his dad's bathrobe is a tent, twirling his grandpa's cane. I am the disenchanted duckling, in the ugly white granny gown with big pockets, holding the Infant of Prague in diapers.

Sister Mary Agnes, cocooned in her habit of black and white, offers last minute warnings. Her starched wimple, too tight around her face, makes her cheeks puffy. I bet she doesn't care how she looks or else she wouldn't be a Benedictine.

Miss Elvira Jean Tippet, the rectory housekeeper, in navy flannel trousers and gray beehive hairdo, sits at the pipe organ. With her habitual vigor, she launches into our opening Advent hymn, "O Come, O Come Emmanuel." Miss Tippet, in my opinion, has a hard life. She cooks and cleans for Father Frank. Without one single day off. Ever. Tonight she plays the church organ good and loud, as she also does every Sunday. People say Miss Tippet marches to the beat of a different drummer. I like that. I like Miss Elvira Jean Tippet. She knows the whole Mass in Latin. Even the priest's parts.

"Blessed Virgin Mother," Sister Mary Agnes yells at me, "stop daydreaming."

"I'm sorry, Sister," I mumble.

She says, "What's that? I can't hear you." Her white wimple tilts in my direction.

"I'm sorry, Sister," I dutifully repeat.

"Sorry isn't good enough, young lady. Pay attention."

Miss Tippet starts in on a thunderous "Silent Night."

Here come the angels, gliding down the aisles. With their precious wings, halos and pretty pageboy curls. Singing their little hearts out. Some even wear glossy pink lipstick. Which is forbidden, but they don't get in trouble. Parents murmur how sweet their darling angels look. Oh, brother, I hate them all.

Except, I do think my friend Patty Ann looks sweet. I'm glad she gets to be an angel because her best talent actually is singing. Unlike some of the other girls, whose best talent is chasing boys.

After the angels arrange themselves on the marble altar steps, the shepherds ride in with their phony sheep. These shepherds, brats who get C's in history and cheat at kickball, are screeching "O Little Town of Bethlehem." Dumb as they come, if you ask me. Which nobody does.

Now Sister gives Joey P. and me a fierce push into the church nave. The organ peals.

The Mother of God enters. Stuck in her role, following conceited old Joey Patrick Purcelli, single file, boys first, walking down St. A's center aisle.

Waving his cane to innkeepers the rest of us can't see, Joseph inquires about rooms at the inn. So far, all according to script.

Casting my eyes down to the floor, I happen to notice that Joseph is wearing loose orange rubber flip-flops that don't fit him any better than his dad's big brown bathrobe. I also see that the hem of that long smelly robe drags on the floor. Right behind Joseph. Right in front of me. Eyes lowered, I clutch the Infant of Prague in the christening blanket, like I've been told to do.

Well, pretty much like I've been told to do.

I get closer to Joseph. And closer. And closer.

Joseph goes down first.

Then his grandpa's cane.

Holy Mother of God, Joseph's cane hits the Infant of Prague.

And the Infant hits the slate floor.

I do not look at Sister Mary Agnes. I know she is looking at me. With a face turning to prunes.

I bend over to pick up the pieces of Baby Jesus, holding my green cat-eye glasses to the bridge of my nose with one hand, scooping up the Christ Child with the other.

But thank God, and I mean that literally, the christening blanket has saved the Infant of Prague.

Well, most of him. He did break a leg.

I lift up the left leg of Baby Jesus. At least it's a clean break. Then I pick up the rest of him. I put Jesus' left leg in the pocket of my great big Blessed Virgin Mother granny gown. It's a good thing we have Elmer's glue at home.

60

Following a pained and slow march, Joseph and I make it to the foot of the altar. Wide-eyed angels part to let us pass, then flock, more or less, to either side of us.

From the pulpit, Father Frank coughs to get everybody's attention. Then he proclaims that Our Savior is born this night, laid in a manger, no room at the inn. Etcetera, etcetera.

As rehearsed, I put my Infant of Prague in a heap of pine straw piled on the sanctuary floor. You can't tell Baby Jesus only has one leg.

In come the Wise Men.

So far, I've played my part. Truly, I have. But the entrance of the Wise Men takes the cake. The way I figure it, this play is historically inaccurate. We all know it took the Wise Men a few days, at the very least, to get themselves to Bethlehem. The Feast of the Epiphany is not celebrated on Christmas Day, is it? Clearly, Sister Mary Agnes is playing fast and loose with the facts.

As I kneel, fed up with trying to look holy, it occurs to me that maybe the role of the Mother of God really is a big deal. She just got a bad script.

"Sister Mary Agnes," I say to myself, "this play is all wrong. It's not fair. You cannot give the Mother of God a part with nothing to say and some dead nun's nightgown to wear."

Think about it. A whole Bible but Mary never gets to speak. Not one word? Even when her kid is born? I don't believe it. Who wrote this Book anyway? Cherubim and Seraphim?

I have had enough. And, as I have been told many times, I am no angel.

I stand up. I speak up, in my loudest voice.

"Joseph," I bark, pointing to Joey Patrick Purcelli in his Cat in the Hat turban, "We need to build this baby a crib. Go get some sticks, fella."

Joey P. looks like he swallowed a dead frog. So does Sister Mary Agnes.

I continue, growling, "I am God's Mother. My son is not sleeping on your dirty mulch."

The church freezes. For a moment it truly is a silent night.

Then I shout in song to the farthest reaches of the pews, "Joy to the World." Tuneless, but very loud.

Miss Elvira Jean Tippet quickly backs me up on organ.

The Blessed Virgin Mother is heard.

#

After the play, Sister Mary Agnes sentences me to detention every Friday afternoon until Easter. Plus, I will never be in a grade school play again. Oh boo-ho. Like I care.

Yeah, I know, Baby Jesus didn't get a crib, I didn't get to be an angel, but the Blessed Virgin Mother got a voice. So did I, sisters and brothers, so did I.

The lesson I learned in a fifth grade Christmas play, in 1962, is that you don't have to accept the role you're given. That lesson has brought me more happiness than any set of angel wings ever could. After all, I'm no angel.

THE END

Mary Alice Dixon

Mary Alice Dixon is a former attorney and graduate of Vassar College, Yale University, and Wake Forest University School of Law. For many years she ran her own law practice in Charlotte, North Carolina where she served as court-appointed counsel and GAL in Mecklenburg County juvenile court.

Prior to law, Mary Alice was a professor of architectural history. She taught at UNC-Charlotte, Chongqing Institute of Architecture and Engineering (China), and the University of Minnesota.

Mary Alice has published professionally in architectural journals and written more legal briefs than she can count. Her first love is creative writing, to which she recently returned full-time. Currently at work on a collection of short stories and poetry, she belongs to Charlotte Writer's Club and the North Carolina Poetry Society.

A long-time hospice volunteer, Mary Alice delights in reading poetry to the dying, grateful for the lessons this teaches about what really matters.

The Dog's His

By Jamie Enslin

Totaling up the dogs big and small living on the farm we count hundreds. Hundreds! Gazing in bewilderment we truly behold more than are plausible. They rush or dally about, they squeal and bark eagerly, and every one of them wags, there is non-stop wagging and wonderfully they form a breathtaking flurry of white commotion.

Within minutes of our arrival we are led to a room reserved for puppies. Hurriedly I situate myself in the middle of the jumbled, ever-shifting confusion. Nearby the mother dogs lie, always at the ready, but selfishly I keep my gaze solely on the babies. They tumble about, climb on each another's heads, backs, faces. They intertwine and tangle and despite a fleeting few remain a tousled, muddled beautiful blob.

They have an abundance of skin on their tiny frames, the puppies, and their fur is as soft as feather down. Some scarcely walk and after a few steps their feet slip, legs sprawl and they land on their bellies so that, with their heads included, they produce a star pattern on the floor. Then, it is only with assistance can right themselves.

When you hold the puppies they droop, like a bunny droops. They chatter and some trickle pee from excitement and due to infancy. Inherently they radiate every dimension of life. Contentedly I lie down and let them "maul" away.

I am the giant in Lilliput and would voluntarily be tied to the spot for eternity.

And the most extraordinary thing of all! Is that one of these puppies will come live at our house! My big brother gets to select a puppy!

I'm confident he will settle on a good one and, thankfully, all of us, any one of us, have my parent's permission to talk to the puppy, even pet the puppy, but the choosing of the puppy? That's my brother's privilege. His honor and his treat.

Because the pup will belong to him.

When home we construct a fenced in area in our basement. It has blankets and there are newspapers spread about. He doesn't know yet to "go" outside. We put a cardboard box in his newly- erected pen so he has a comforting enclosure. The clock we install is so the ticking sound will remind him of his mother's heartbeat. I talk to him, pet him and watch over him readily. It's okay if I do this as long as I remember he is not my dog.

Later, at bedtime, I beg and I plead. I want to stay next to my brother's dog through the night. My mother says I won't sleep properly. I sleep in my bed and I dream of my brother's dog.

With my father's help my brother makes a doghouse which he places in his room. His dog doesn't take to it though, instead he curls up on my brother's bed. My little brother and my sister think the dog is cute. When requested they respect my brother's wishes and leave the dog be. They defer to our brother concerning the dog. Freely they acknowledge the dog belongs solely to him.

West Highland Terriers are smart. Tempting him with vanilla cookies I teach him tricks. When done he can roll over, beg, dance, turn a circle and shake hands.

So smart.

Although I am reminded over and over not to, I feed him bits from the dinner table. I'm artful and mostly get away with it. Every time, in anticipation, he waits silently next to my chair and fixes his eyes keenly on me.

He is smart!

His dish sits in the corner of the kitchen alongside the cat's. We feed both the animals together but each day, it is only after our "Tom" has finished his meal, only after he is done grooming himself carefully and methodically, just after he stretches forward and back unhurriedly, and only after he wanders leisurely on, tail up, never glancing back, only then does the dog have permission to the corner. Then, impatiently, as if he worries the cat may change his mind and refuse access, my brother's dog sprints. He slurps down his food in an instant, a mere heartbeat, then wagging, always wagging, he pads away.

My brother gets older, busier. Baseball, basketball, guitar and friends dominate his life. He doesn't have much time for his dog. Therefore, in sensing my opportunity for real, I zoom in all set for the rescue.

Happily I take on the responsibility of feeding my brother's dog and brushing him. I towel him down after his baths. Now every night he curls up close and sleeps on my bed. When our cat is not outdoors longing for a fight he sleeps there too. Thankfully my parents realize they cannot deny the dog this, as long as I promise, of course, to never forget the dog belongs to my brother.

At this stage, the age I am now, I prefer the company of my brother's dog more than that of my friends, really my siblings for that matter. I am ten. During the winter we have deep snow and I spend hours creating paths for him to navigate. Westies are short, maybe a foot tall. He is unable to see over the snowy hedges I create, but he follows behind within my maze wagging his tail eagerly, fervently. If I had a tail I would wag mine too.

The four of us, the four siblings, each crouch in a corner of our living room. We have placed my brother's dog in the center where he looks around bewildered. Nevertheless, he waits sitting at attention. On the count of three we all call to him, simultaneously we instruct him to come. Without delay he runs in my direction, without pause he lands in my lap. My siblings demand a rematch but the outcome duplicates the first. My smile is enormous, gargantuan! I am filled with joy and inner warmth. Openly I gloat. But, walking away, my siblings make certain I understand that, even so, the dog remains the special pet of our older brother.

The cat sits on the fence in the back scrutinizing the grassy expanse beyond. He is the color of dark caramel and rich earth. He is massive, he is quick, and he is a ferocious hunter. The dog, belonging to my brother, is outside the open gate beyond the yard, wandering, sniffing, wagging.

Our cat glances over from time to time, watches the dog. Looks bored. Another dog, a large shepherd, enters the cat's field of vision. The stranger dog focuses on the smaller and begins a soundless, deliberate approach in his direction. Then swiftly, unpredictably, the great dog lunges, firmly snatching the littler by the neck. Next he shoots down the field passing close to the fence below the spot where our cat watches over. He carries my brother's dog in his jaws.

We hear the cries and rush out back, my sister, my mother and me. My sister and mother are alarmed, fretful, deeply upset, and I am hysterical. In formidable contrast our cat is composed but alert, calm but vigilant, seemingly aloof, but fiercely engaged.

Gallantly he vaults off his fence perch leaping onto the predator dog's back. With outstretched claws he scratches, gashes and digs grooves into the dog's hide. Immediately the wolf-like shepherd shrieks and releases his hostage. Nevertheless, the cat continues his ride piercing the dog's back further until he draws blood. Then, seemingly content with his handiwork, he springs to the ground and is gone.

We rush to where our little dog whimpers and lies still. But, as we approach, he cannot control his tail. It thumps rhythmically, steadily against the hard earth. He basks in our kisses, our pampering.

Once inside I make a bed out of pillows and blankets. I remain with him, pet him, hum to him.   I get up next and make to leave the room. His head follows me, eyes my whereabouts, he seems to search my face for intention, worry over where I may go. Then, likely sensing his nursing care has come to its end, he pops up quickly. He wags excitedly and rushes to catch up.

Later at feeding time the cat takes longer than ever with his routine before letting the dog scramble to his corner dish. But that evening he curls up close to the dog on my bed and we all sleep peacefully.

He spends three days at the vet's, my brother's dog. My mother assures "he will be just fine, he will come home better than ever!" At recess I rush to the school office. Yes, I can use the phone. By the third morning my mother knows it will be me and she picks up at once. She reassures, the dog is doing well. We bring him home that afternoon. He is better than ever.

I'm in college when he dies. Although my siblings also live close by I am the one my parents call. They invite me to dinner and they break the news. They know the news will touch deeply and they comfort me.

Openly, and genuinely, they understand that I spent a lifetime loving a dog that was never mine.

Jamie Enslin

Jamie divides her time between Seattle, WA and the mountains of Idaho. She was first inspired to write stories by her psychologist, after which, writing for her became a passion. She is currently working on a book of historical Fiction titled: Pen Pals. A story set during the time of the Algerian war of independence from France.

Jamie holds degrees in French Studies and Communications from the University of WA, Seattle, WA

In addition to writing she is an artist of collage and encaustic.

You can follow Jamie on Twitter at: @jjkctjbm

The Narcissist

By Jackie Ross Flaum

Germantown Detective Alvin Benson knocked on the
hospital room door to fulfill a promise. The widow knew Dan
Anderson died, so the Tennessee policeman expected his visit would
be less stressful than a death notification — and quicker. He
introduced himself to the family and plunged in, "Mrs. Anderson,
I'm sorry to have to tell you that your husband died from poisoning."

"P-poison? W-What?" Mercy Anderson's raspy voice drifted
from the bed. Lines gouged her forehead and limp brown hair
straggled around high cheek bones made more pronounced by rapid
weight loss.

The suburban police department considered the death of its
former alderman solved. However, the chief wanted to give the
family closure, comfort, and few details before it hit the press. Since
he was known as a nice guy and only involved in the periphery of
the investigation, Benson became the ideal candidate for the courtesy
visit.

"Mr. Anderson swallowed a massive dose of poison."
Benson rubbed his nose. The aroma of the flowers in the room even
overpowered the antiseptic hospital smell.

"Massive dose," echoed Priscilla Murphy, Mercy's younger sister from Atlanta.

The silence stretched. The young detective's thoughts drifted to a planned anniversary celebration with his wife. He prayed this quiet meant the family needed no more information. He wanted to be on time to dinner.

"I-I don't understand," Mercy finally stammered. "It doesn't — did someone call Dan's brother? Priscilla, did you call George?"

"Finally. George will be here soon." Priscilla held the arms of her chair in a white-knuckle grip. "You know, sweetie, I was sick as a dog too."

She looked better than the week Benson saw her in a hospital bed. Today she wore enough make-up to appear healthy but not painted. Her black curly hair, washed and swept back, made her round face seem longer and complimented her hazel eyes.

"Oh-h yes. You were sick too." Mercy's eyebrows came together as though she was trying to recall more. "Wh-what happened?"

"Mrs. Anderson, you, your sister, and your husband ingested the same toxin." Benson said. No one looked comforted.

"Toxin?" Mercy felt around the top of the bedside table for her glasses. Once she put them on, she cast about the room as if searching for answers.

"Mercy, you've been so ill. We didn't tell you anything. We almost lost you." Priscilla rose, pulled the covers to her sister's chin, and tucked in loose ends. "Some policemen asked you about the night we got sick. Then the nice police chief and a chaplain came by to tell you Dan died, don't you remember? They promised someone would be around to explain. I told them it wasn't necessary, but here is Detective Benson."

Mercy's blank expression told Benson she did not have a clue what Priscilla meant.

"Mercy? Y-you look shaky. Hold my hand." Priscilla licked her lips and massaged her sister's knuckles.

A police presence unsettled people, and at over six-feet-tall Benson feared he appeared even more intimidating in the room of flowers and frail women. "We did some checking once we confirmed Mr. Anderson's cause of death."

"And?" Priscilla moved to the edge of her chair.

"Mrs. Anderson, you complained to your doctor of stomach cramps, exhaustion, headaches, and tingling in your hands and feet in the weeks prior to your sister's visit. He diagnosed a virus. And your regular manicurist remarked on white stripes across your fingernails."

"I remember she made a fuss about my nails. And th-those awful headaches," murmured Mercy.

"You suffered arsenic poisoning."

Priscilla let out a whoosh of air.

"How?" Mercy whimpered.

"We believe your husband tried to kill you."

"Wrong. You're wrong." Mercy's face sagged until she looked decades older than forty-one.

"Your husband and sister had lycorine poisoning. You also had arsenic in your blood. You suffered from two types of poison." He sighed.

"Lycorine poisoning." Priscilla parroted.

"Dan loved me," sobbed Mercy.

Benson lost the illusion he could spare anyone's feelings. It wasn't looking good for his anniversary dinner either.

"Why poison me?" Priscilla pushed herself from the chair toward the bedside. Her ringlets bounced around cheeks now bright red.

"You were, ah, collateral damage, Mrs. Murphy," said Benson.

Priscilla swayed. "I don't -- arsenic and, did you say lycori —?"

"Dan was not capable of what you're saying, detective. He was a kind, loving, decent man. He enjoyed old cars, baseball, cooking . . . He-he did most of the cooking." Mercy's hand trembled as she brushed her hair back. Tears stained her glasses and cheeks. "He bought me diamond earrings for my birthday."

"Mercy, please . . . You'll make me cry too, sweetie," Priscilla sniffed.

In most hospital rooms the white light over the bed shone on the patient, but this one flooded the ceiling, giving the pastel-colored room a soothing glow. Benson hoped the calm would spread over its weepy occupants. All he could think to say was, "It's good your sons were spending the night with friends."

"Teenage boys are always out with their friends." Mercy coughed.

"I talked to them. Nice young men. I got married a year ago." Benson sensed a slight chance to mention his anniversary and leave.

"The way the police questioned me and Mercy –." Priscilla huffed.

Mercy lifted her glasses to swipe a tear and the oxygen tube dislodged from her nose. She needed both hands to set it right. The IV in her arm jiggled, setting off an alarm which brought a nurse. In the confusion Benson checked his watch and frowned.

"Mrs. Anderson, I'm sorry if our questions upset you or your sister. It's standard procedure to check persons closest to the vic, uh, person who died. Plus, poison is the weapon of choice for ladies," Benson said. "And you are an avid gardener."

"So am I," Priscilla's busy hands fiddled with covers or fussed with tulips near the bed.

"Mrs. Anderson had a motive and access to poison. We also checked on you, Mrs. Murphy. Your background, financials, and friends." Benson used his quiet, earnest voice.

"Why would I kill Dan? He was — and why would Mercy kill him, for goodness sake?"

"Oh, Priscilla," Mercy breathed. "Let it go."

Benson shrugged. "Maybe Mrs. Anderson had enough of her husband after the incident last month."

A soft whir filled the room as Mercy rolled up the head of her bed. "His one whiskey before dinner became three, and we quarreled. One of our boys called the police. Teenagers. It was so unnecessary."

"You never told me you needed the police, Mercy," Priscilla whispered.

"Mrs. Anderson, our records show not one but two domestic disturbance calls to your residence," Benson pointed out. "On the second visit they arrested your husband for spitting on the responding officer,"

Priscilla closed her eyes. "Dear God."

"Ma'am, you aren't alone. Most victims of domestic abuse are embarrassed, make excuses for —."

"Detective! Dan did not raise his hand to me. He was a very large man. I told him all the time he didn't know how strong he was." Mercy smiled as though a pleasant memory flitted through her head.

The detective caught a glimpse of Priscilla. Mouth open, she groped behind her for the hospital chair she'd been sitting in. She hadn't come from Atlanta for a visit in months, although phone records showed the sisters spoke frequently. Typical for an abusive husband to isolate his wife. Maybe he never hit her, but Dan Anderson abused Mercy.

"Thank you for coming, Detective," Priscilla said softly.

"Detective, you think he was awful because you heard about his argument with the buyer, right?" Mercy demanded. "You were

79

there, Priscilla. It was the day you arrived. A silly misunderstanding over an order at my shop, Mercy Me Clothing."

Somewhere outside the hospital room an alarm beep sounded. Nurses scurried in the hallway. Carts clattered.

"Priscilla?" Mercy tried to rise on her elbow.

"I'm not defending him on this one, Mercy. He called you a 'damn cretin' and 'a shitty manager' in front of the New York buyer. He did those things all the times I was with you. You used to tell me he did it to the boys too."

A knock, then a tall man with a square jaw, piercing brown eyes and dark hair lavishly streaked with white poked his head inside. "Mercy?"

"Oh, George. You came," she sighed.

"Of course, I came. And brought you your favorite flowers. How are you? Hi, Priscilla." The man placed a decorative pot of yellow daffodils on the table next to Mercy.

While Benson absorbed the irony of the gift, the man shifted his tan overcoat to his other arm and leaned over the bed to kiss Mercy on the cheek. "I'd have been here sooner, but I had the flu. I love you beyond measure, and I'm so sorry."

"Detective Benson, this is George Anderson, Dan's older brother. He's a psychology professor at the University of Kentucky. Detective Benson is investigating Dan's death." Priscilla stood to make the introductions.

The strong resemblance between Mercy's two sons and George Anderson startled Benson.

"Investigate?" George's eyebrows arched.

"He poisoned himself." The words seemed to drain Priscilla. "He tried to murder Mercy with arsenic and ended up killing himself — and almost killing Mercy and me —with lycorine. Detective Benson just explained."

Benson cleared his throat. "That's our line of thinking."

"I understand, Detective," Mercy said. "But I don't like it. Thank you for coming."

"H-how do you know someone didn't kill him? Poison all of them?" George's hand grasped Mercy's. "The gardener? Or the housekeeper?"

"Not Jose, our gardener. Dan flew his son from Florida to St. Jude in Memphis for cancer treatment. Jose worshipped Dan," Mercy offered.

"We talked to all your help," said Benson.

"How about his ex-business partner? Dan sued him for his share of the partnership," George pressed.

"He was out of town when the murder and attempted murders happened." Benson watched George bring Mercy's hand to his lips for a tender kiss.

Benson had not been in on these interviews, but he knew Dan's former real estate partner called him a fabulous salesman. The old partner claimed the chaos of working with Dan wasn't worth the money he generated. When a project failed, it was never Dan's fault, and he was quick to involve a lawyer. Moreover, Dan's temperament unsettled everyone from his ex-partner to city officials. He cursed a

81

political opponent over a policy disagreement, stomped out of a Board of Alderman meeting, and sued a neighbor who misplaced his trash can.

"Only people he claimed to love were his family." George dropped Mercy's hand long enough to thrust his coat on a chair in the corner with more anger than sorrow. "Though he did enjoy charity and garnering the slavish gratitude of those less fortunate."

A part of Benson wanted to learn more. Nobody was as awful as Dan Anderson seemed. While George occupied the women, Benson stole a peek at his watch.

"It took me years to understand Dan. I think that's why I changed my college major after we broke up, Mercy. I longed to know why he derived pleasure from chaos. Nothing was ever good enough for him, no amount of attention was sufficient." George paced by the bedside.

Something zinged in Benson's gut. Dan's brother was Mercy's rejected suitor? Surely someone in his department explored the relationship.

"He treated our parents like they had a pot of gold hidden from him ... or possessed extra arms and legs to serve him," George continued. "After your boys were born, Mercy, he used to tell our mother she'd never see her grandchildren when she crossed him."

"I know he was gruff sometimes. Bu-t, he renovated the back room for them when they visited. He planned for them to retire here," Mercy snuffled. "And when your wife died, who was the first person at your door?"

"Dan was a great help. I was really . . ." George threw up his hands.

Benson didn't want to delay his departure, but he had to know. "How long have you been a widower, Mr. Anderson?"

"A year and a half. Car accident." George gazed at Mercy.

"Children?" asked Benson.

"Sadly, no. My students and my nephews are my children," George said. "You?"

"No." And he might never have any if he didn't leave for dinner soon.

"Dan was easy to hate sometimes. He could be downright mean," Mercy said. "But those times were few. He was charming, clever, kind to a fault. He'd do anything for you."

"You know I cared for him. He was my brother," George said. "However, life with him was living on the edge of a knife. You understand — did you ever get a therapist?"

Mercy tugged the covers up to her chin and didn't meet his eye.

"You know, I can't remember a holiday or family get-together Dan didn't ruin by picking a fight or causing a scene," George mumbled. "He didn't get the expensive train set he wanted one Christmas, pushed the one he got away, and pouted. I remember how it hurt Mom's feelings."

"Will you help me plan the funeral, George?" Mercy's lip quivered.

With a sigh George nodded. "I cannot believe Dan poisoned anyone."

"We found white arsenic powder in his toolbox when we searched Mr. Anderson's garage," Benson said.

For a moment George gawked. "Sorry. I was trying to imagine Dan using tools or owning a toolbox. Where would he find arsenic? And the other poison, lycorine? Isn't that from --."

"Daffodils, George. It's poison from daffodil bulbs." Benson stared at Priscilla, so she added, "Told you I was a gardener. Narcissus poeticus is the deadliest type."

"Oh my God. Dan was a narcissist." George ran a hand through his hair.

Somehow it fit. It felt right to Benson. His left foot edged toward the door. Priscilla examined the tile floor. Mercy raised her glasses and wiped her eyes with a tissue from the bedside dispenser.

It was too damn perfect. Cursing himself Benson asked, "Did you know he was a narcissist, Mrs. Anderson?"

She looked at George. "Did you ever tell me?"

"Perhaps I should have," said George. "I was afraid I'd offend. I mentioned it to our mother once, and she became angry."

Priscilla glanced at Benson and frowned. She asked George, "Are narcissists, ah, dangerous?"

"There is a correlation between sociopaths and narcissistic behavior," George admitted. "The famous murderer Ted Bundy, for example, was a narcissist."

Mercy moaned.

84

"Mrs. Anderson, your husband ordered arsenic powder two months ago and dozens of the flower bulbs last week from a laptop accessible by only his fingerprint." Once its contents were analyzed, Benson understood why Dan was so protective of his computer. "Your elder son saw him cutting vegetables for soup."

"Dan cooked dinner most nights." Mercy ignored her sister. "And I bet he ordered those bulbs as a gift for me."

George's palm shot straight out. "Excuse me . . . Dan tried to poison Mercy with arsenic and, failing there, he cooked poison soup? Is that what you're implying? Poison from daffodils?"

"The bulbs can be mistaken for onions." Benson found it hard to believe himself, but toxicology reports didn't lie. He'd done a little research and discovered that in 2009 some English schoolchildren ate soup with one daffodil bulb in it and became very ill. From the residue of the soup the Andersons and Mrs. Murphy ate, more than a few bulbs hit the poison pot.

"W-hy would he poison the soup then eat so much he'd die?" George persisted. Benson wondered the same thing.

"He was drunk," Priscilla drawled.

Mercy's finger wagged in the air. "He had a cold and took medicine for it."

"Was he allergic to anything?" wondered Benson.

"All kinds of plants and grasses." George volunteered.

"I meant he had allergies," Mercy amended. "I love flowers. It was a challenge to keep those he was allergic to out of the house."

85

"Sweetie, he had two drinks before dinner. Remember?" Priscilla rose and came to the bedside. "You suggested he not have any whiskey. He called you a fucking idiot and drank two more shots."

"Come on, it was a fun evening. We laughed and laughed," Mercy said. "Dan was so witty. Everything we said he turned into a joke."

"We believe his congestion, and the whisky, kept him from tasting the soup or realizing how much he ingested." Benson declared. The coroner found alcohol in Anderson, and antihistamine in amounts consistent with a cold or allergy sufferer.

"His beef vegetable soup was bitter. He acted so proud of the awful stuff," Priscilla said. "I ate enough to be polite and, thank God, Mercy ate even less. I didn't notice how much Dan ate. You have been so kind to come, Detective, we don't want to keep you."

"You are suggesting he suffered from allergies, had a few drinks, and couldn't taste the soup or realize how much he ate?" George's hands went to his hips.

When he said it like that Benson wasn't sure of the department's conclusion, but evidence couldn't be ignored. It was easy to look at the wife for the alderman's murder, but here the detective felt confident. He personally checked on Mrs. Anderson. Based on his interviews with friends, neighbors and business associates she came off as gentle as the flowers she loved.

"After dinner Dan watched a ball game while Priscilla and I cleaned the kitchen. He went to bed before we did," Mercy recalled.

"When Priscilla and I came upstairs, I heard him groaning, so I slept in the guest room. With all the vomiting and diarrhea, I thought we all had a stomach virus, so I told the boys to spend another night with their friends."

As the police pieced together what happened, the next day Priscilla managed to dial 9-1-1. By the time help arrived it was too late for Dan. His wife moaned down the hall dehydrated and barely conscious.

"Personally, I think the liquor showed Dan had a heart." Priscilla announced. "He knew what he was doing was wrong and had to dull his conscience."

"You believe the police have the right story?" George leaned toward Priscilla.

Mercy wailed something like 'no.'

"In a way, I agree with Mercy. In Dan's mind all his decisions were right. He had the ability to justify whatever he said or did. Yet . . ." George rubbed the back of his neck. "Dan loved himself too much to risk death — or even make himself sick."

Benson had not heard any analysis like this before. If George was right, then Dan Anderson's action made no sense. Unless the lead detective in the case, not George, hit it right.

"A near death is a good way to get investigators to suspect someone else." Benson repeated the official theory. "It was a gamble that didn't pay off."

"You know." Mercy shuddered.

Priscilla swallowed hard, her eyes wide. "Know what?"

Mercy and the detective exchanged glances.

"Dan . . . Dan gambled online. On the precious computer he wouldn't let anyone touch. I- I noticed him taking money from my store. He denied it, called me a . . . a lousy businesswoman." Mercy wet her lips. "Could I have some water?"

Priscilla jumped to reach the tan plastic and Styrofoam water pitcher, poured a shaky stream of ice water into a plastic cup on the tray by the bed, and fumbled to find a straw. "Here, sweetie."

George shook his head. "I bet he was a high roller too."

Benson decided he'd more than done his duty here. Sometimes bizarre cases were just bizarre. One more piece of business and he would run all the way to Chez Martinique where his wife waited.

"Mr. Anderson had a life insurance policy."

"We each had a policy. I think we bought them when the first child arrived. Don't most couples?" Mercy raised the head of her bed a little higher.

"A million dollars each is rather large." Benson said.

"I watch TV -- nobody collects insurance on murder," Priscilla scoffed.

"Unless he made it look like everyone was accidentally poisoned. I don't mean to tell you your business, detective, but it seems far-fetched," George said.

Benson nodded. "A killer cannot collect on a life insurance policy, true. Mr. Anderson didn't count on killing himself — just his wife and sister-in-law."

"Why did he eat so much? I'm afraid I can't swallow your theory, Detective." George pulled on one ear. "I wish I could."

Grieving family members could not help rehashing police facts and often tortured themselves with "if only." Benson decided to leave on a high note.

"You might have a life insurance claim, Mrs. Anderson, since we will likely rule your husband's death accidental."

The reaction to the news sucked the air out of the room. Benson seized his chance to grasp the hospital door handle.

"T-Thank you, Detective," Priscilla stammered.

George grabbed his coat. "I'll be back. I'll go to the house, see the boys and bring them up after dinner. You rest. I'll stay with you until you ask me to leave."

Mercy sniffled. "Thanks, George."

"I loved him, Mercy. But he was a classic example of a narcissist. Truthfully, I was a little afraid of him." George's voice caught.

He opened the door for Benson and the two men stood aside to allow a nurse to come in. The nurse checked Mercy's vital signs, monitored her IV, adjusted the oxygen flow, and left. Priscilla walked with deliberate step to the door and closed it. Then she stopped at the foot of her sister's bed.

"It was close, Mercy. I was scared we'd overdone it."

"I think your charcoal pills helped."

Priscilla patted her middle. "I always keep them for my sour stomach. Charcoal absorbs a lot of toxins."

"He tried to kill me, Priscilla." Mercy's jaw clenched. "I'm glad we struck before he slipped me more arsenic."

"You were lucky. What are the chances you'd find the arsenic in the tool kit and recognize it?"

"I had no idea what it was. I saw the bottle when I searched for a nail to hang a new picture," Mercy said. "But I was feeling sick so I Googled my symptoms. Headache and dizziness are common, but the metallic taste and garlicky breath? You know how I hate garlic. Arsenic poison. I thought of the bottle and knew."

"I'm glad you asked me to come. Therapy paid off, you're a strong woman, not a victim."

"His hand brushed me when I grabbed his cell away," Mercy mumbled. "He suffered so -- I nearly gave the phone to him. Heck, I was sick enough to call for help myself."

"I slipped those peeled bulbs in the soup with no qualms," Priscilla said.

"He was smart —." Mercy grimaced. "Smart enough to wiggle out of an attempted murder charge."

"Did you lose much setting him up as a gambler?"

"A few thousand. The tough part was swiping his passwords."

"How?" Priscilla asked.

"He had a fingerprint access on his laptop. I brought the computer to the bedside one night when he'd had more than one drink."

Priscilla breathed. "Risky."

Mercy sat up straighter. "You think his allergy flare-up was an accident? I sprinkled all the plants he was allergic to in floral arrangements around our house. Finally, his nose ran like a spigot."

Priscilla leaned on the hospital bed. "I'll go home to Atlanta after the funeral. George will stay."

"The whole thing took more out of me than I planned. I've never been so sick and . . ." Mercy regarded her sister with amusement. "And I wouldn't mind if George stays awhile — if he doesn't ask questions."

Priscilla grinned.

"I'll keep my word," Mercy hurried on. "You can buy your floral shop when the insurance comes through."

She chuckled, "I damn sure won't sell daffodils."

++

Jackie Ross Flaum

Native Kentuckian Jackie Ross Flaum is a former reporter for *The Hartford Courant* in Hartford, Ct. She moved to Memphis with her husband and two daughters in 1983 then served as publicist for the Memphis Symphony Orchestra, communications manager for Memphis City Schools, and free-lance speech writer/publicist for such corporations as Federal Express. When she retired, she abandoned reality and now writes fiction, especially mysteries. Her first short story appears in the award-winning anthology *Elmwood Stories to Die For*. Another, "Gummies," won first Short Story Land's prize for June fiction, and a third story "Cover," based on her up-coming novel *Justice Tomorrow*, will appear in a fall anthology from Dingbat Publishing. When she is not coming up with ways for fictional characters to commit felonies, she plays bridge, swims, reads, or takes one or more of her five grandchildren to get snow cones. Join her on Facebook at Novelist Jackie Ross Flaum

Saint Paul's Living Nativity

By Jay Gilbert

Adventure, risk taking, and "Well, I thought it was a good idea at the time," was embedded in our family DNA. Mom and Dad taught us, through their actions and attitude, the simple philosophy that life is meant to be lived fully—every day. Growing up on a farm in Minnesota brought ample opportunity for some crazy family memories. Here is the tale of one such adventure.

*****

One of our father's early goals was to have enough horse backs for five boys' butts. We especially needed them for long rides in the country with the entire gang. Our equine collection primarily consisted of Quarter Horses. Quarter Horses are some of the calmest, most well-behaved horses in the world, they are perfect for families with lots of kids. Unfortunately, Dad didn't stop there. No, he thought it would be perfect to round out the collection with a Shetland pony. Shetlands are the alter ego of Quarter Horses. Stubborn as mules, they wouldn't hesitate to give you, or another horse twice their size, a good swift kick for no good reason. Originally from the Shetland Islands, these little ponies had short legs, stout, muscular bodies, and long tails that almost touch the ground. Strong as bucking broncos, they could throw an adult rider off their little backs as if they were a ragdoll. Still, with five boys to feed, money was tight. We would have to find a good deal before we could add a pony to the herd.

While reading the paper one quiet Sunday morning, my father spotted an ad for a pony. "For Sale: One-year-old Shetland pony, white with black head. $65.00." Well, the paper had barely hit the floor by the time Dad was calling the number in the ad. He knew a good deal when he saw it, and a one-year-old pony for sixty-five dollars was an excellent deal.

"Hello," Dad said, "I'm calling about the ad you have in today's paper for a Shetland pony. Do you still have him? You do. Can we come to see him today? We can? Great! What's your address?"

Apparently, the owners had won the pony in a raffle at the local fair. They were an older couple with no children and no place to keep a pony. In retrospect, we should have questioned their enthusiasm to meet us on such short notice... on a Sunday.

We gathered a few supplies, packed some sandwiches, and off we went for a relatively short Sunday drive of two hours to the rural town of Princeton, MN. Dad seemed to have an inner compass and being a native of Duluth for over forty years, he knew every backroad, town, and lake in Northern Minnesota. He never needed a map to get there—wherever there was. Upon our arrival, he parked the car and greeted the man on the porch. "Hi, I called this morning about the pony you have for sale."

"Yes, sir," the owner said. "He's out back."

Rounding the corner between the house and garage, there stood Jiggers, the Shetland pony. He had a gleaming white body, jet-black head, and the mischievous eyes of a Labrador puppy. One-year-old, fit and trim, Jiggers was everything we had hoped for and more. Dad didn't even try to negotiate.

"We'll take him," he said, pulling sixty-five dollars in cash out of his wallet and handing it to the owner.

"I'll get his papers for you," the owner said. Upon his return from the house, he gave Jiggers' registration papers to Dad. "When would you like to pick him up?"

"We'll take him right now," Dad said.

"Take him? How?" he asked incredulously. "You don't have a trailer!"

"Just watch."

Dad took Jiggers by the lead rope and led him out from the backyard.

"Open both back doors on the car," he firmly instructed my oldest brother. "Stand behind the open door and hold still so you don't spook him."

The rest of us just stood there and watched in disbelief as our father walked the pony from the house to the rear of the car and right through the open back door.

"Shut the door when both back hooves are in the car." He instructed as he stepped out the other side, turned, and shut the other door. It was one smooth operation of walking Jiggers up into the space between the front and back bench seats of the Ford. The former owner and his wife just stood there, jaws dropped, with looks of utter disbelief on their faces as the rest of us quickly jumped through the tailgate to the "way" back of the station wagon. Then we slowly drove off, all seven of us, plus a pony looking out the window. On the drive back to Duluth, we laughed when people in passing cars pointed and said...THERE'S A PONY IN THAT CAR!

Buying Jiggers and bringing him home in the car was a great adventure. Little did we know it would lead to our most famous, or more accurately, infamous family fiasco. Each year for Christmas, our church, Saint Paul's Episcopal, had a living Nativity which displayed a life-size wooden manger, bales of straw, and a cast of kids and farm animals. The cast members were volunteered by over-eager parishioners, especially moms, who placed an unwarranted amount of social value on such things. A large doll dressed as baby Jesus completed the scene. A real baby in the manger would have frozen to death. This particular Christmas the priest chose our family for the nativity. So special an honor you simply didn't pass up the opportunity due to a little cold weather. You might never get the chance again. I shudder at the thought!

Our family's contribution included my older brothers as part of the cast, bales of straw, and our cute little Shetland pony. Jigger's small size and snow-white winter coat of hair and black head seemed like a perfect fit for the annual living Nativity located next to the front doors of Saint Paul's Episcopal Church.

The operational logistics of getting five boys dressed and ready for church on a normal Sunday took incredible effort and patience from our mother, let alone on a painfully cold Christmas Eve with a pony and bales of straw loaded in a horse...err...pony trailer hitched to the station wagon. How she managed to get five boys suited up, into the car, and finally seated in a church pew each Sunday without a piece of dirt, hay, or anything else we could find to toss at each other was a minor miracle. She deserved a medal.

So down the driveway rolled the family station wagon with pony in tow. Swan Lake to Arrowhead and then down the steep hill upon which the city of Duluth was built. Saint Paul's was almost at the bottom, close to Lake Superior in an affluent part of town. Once there, Dad parked the car on a side street adjacent to the church grounds. My older brothers, costumed as the three Wiseman, assembled in front of the manger while Dad unloaded Jiggers. Everything proceeded smoothly until another family, also chosen to participate that year, arrived with their donkey. We heard Dad say, "Uh ...oh." Mom seemed unconcerned as she admired the nativity with us little guys for a few freezing minutes. The snow crunched under our feet as we headed inside, shivering.

We were early, and as a result, got one of the coveted front pews. Mom beamed with pride and joy as fellow parishioners made their way into church. Adoring smiles and nods of approval for the wonderful living nativity scene, graciously floated over the pews straight to our family.

The service commenced with all the pomp and circumstance of this hallowed occasion. The church overflowed with both regular and seasonal Christians in attendance. Many stood in the back and along the sides. All was simply perfect. Or so it seemed.

A pastoral silence poured over the congregation like a warm blanket. The priest, standing at the pulpit, squared up the papers upon which were his notes for the sermon. Glancing down to collect his thoughts, then looking up and out over the congregation, he prepared to speak. All eyes were focused on him. A warm, mindful quiet washed over the parishioners, as he opened his mouth to speak and out blurted
HEEHAW...WHINNEY!

The experienced clergyman started anew. Head up; look out, open mouth and once again *HEEHAW...WHINNEY*, poured out of him like bad karaoke. This time he froze with an expression of "What the heck?" Mom's face had a look of sheer horror. Mortified, staring straight forward, not moving a muscle, silently screaming, "Oh God, no, please, God, no!" We could tell she wanted to slink down under the pew, but she remained steadfast with proper pew posture.

Dad had a look of "Crap, I knew this would happen when I saw that damn donkey!" Maybe, just maybe, that would be the only outburst from the living nativity.

The priest soldiered on, "My friends, we are gathered here on this special day to celebrate the birth of Jesus ... *HEEHAW* ... *WHINNEY* ... Christ."

The priest didn't miss a beat as a loud thud and crashing noise reverberated through the stained-glass windows. But as he continued, the pastor clearly made direct eye contact with Dad, giving him an assertive look of "please do something about this right **now**!" Dad calmly rose and hurried down the excruciatingly long aisle to the main entrance of the church. He must have been fuming inside, "We couldn't sit in the *rear* of the church—NO, that's not good enough for such an occasion!"

All the parishioners did their best to look forward at the pulpit and listen to the priest give his most important sermon of the year. But their attention remained squarely on Dad and the apparent breakdown of peace on earth just outside. I'm certain, were it not for the time and place, everyone would have been right behind him, heading out to see the big fight.

Just as he opened the enormous, wooden front door, which only served to amplify the commotion, one of my brothers shouted, "Jiggers—knock it the hell off!" This unintended message of the Christmas spirit shot through the open door, echoed off the cavernous stone walls of the Cathedral, and hit the pastor's ears like a shotgun blast. Even when the door finally closed, we could still hear Dad say, "Get that damn donkey out of here now!"

Upon reaching the scene of the crime, it became painfully clear that Jiggers was not in the Christmas spirit. He'd attacked the donkey, biting, kicking and generally objecting to the presence of this inferior creature. One of his attempts to kick the donkey missed the mark and hit the manger, breaking it into small pieces of kindling and knocking baby Jesus across the front lawn and headfirst into a snowbank. Dad stopped in his tracks for the briefest of seconds. There, before his anguished eyes, was a smashed nativity, straw strewn everywhere, and baby Jesus half buried with only his little bare feet sticking out of the snow. Tears rolled down Mary's face and froze to her cheeks. Joseph was in shock, and Jiggers and the donkey were still going at each other, kicking, biting, whinnying and heehawing.

Dad took control of the situation, grabbing Jiggers by the halter with such strength and authority the little Shetland knew he was in deep trouble. He led him directly back to the trailer while barking out orders to the boys to chase down the donkey, lift the nativity, pull baby Jesus out of the snowbank, and try to reassemble the splintered wood into something that passed for a manger.

Once the snow settled, cast members back in character and Jiggers safely locked up in pony jail, Dad made his way back into church. Straightening his jacket and tie, he calmly proceeded back up the aisle to the front pew, turned and sat down just as the priest finished the sermon. Almost on cue, the choir broke into an enthusiastic, if not celebratory, rendition of *Joy to the World*. The priest looked at Dad with a reassuring glance that clearly said, "Thank you!"

Moral of the story:
Never mix ponies and donkeys, because our pony will kick your donkey's ass.

Jay Gilbert

Jay Gilbert was born and raised on a farm in Duluth, MN. One of five boys, his father kept them out of trouble (mostly) with a host of daily chores caring for horses, cows, chickens and ducks. If it mooed, clucked or quacked, they had it. If they weren't feeding the animals at the front end, they were shoveling what came out of the back end. His family owned and operated small businesses ranging from a ship chandlery, vacuum shop, stereo store and a motel. Their businesses took them from Minnesota to Illinois and finally Florida. Between farm life and family business, he has collected an eclectic inventory of experiences that are the basis for his stories. Jay lives and writes by the lessons his parents taught him.

Dad always said "Life is not a dress rehearsal. There are no do-overs."

Mom taught us how to say, "Please" and "Thank you" and mean it.

The Trouble With Blooming

By Lisa McCormack

The farm sat in a valley ringed by hills that shielded the white clap-board house, the tilting gray barn, the ponds and pastures of grazing cattle. For Louise, the farm was a magic place, so different from her suburban home. There were no arguing parents, no bullying school kids or homework, just Grandma and Papa, who she loved fiercely. The farm was her kingdom, a place to romp around and be herself, ride the pony, feed cows and chickens and watch soap-operas with Grandma in the afternoons. It was a treasure Louise thought would never change.

But in 1968, the year Louise turned twelve, her world did change. Two political leaders were shot, the Tet Offensive killed thousands of Americans in Vietnam, and Apollo 8 took men to the moon. But on the farm, the changes were mostly in Louise. Grandma noticed Louise's new tiny breasts right away, even though Louise always wore a loose T-shirt under her cut-off overalls.

"Look at you child, already blooming into a young woman," Grandma said, as though Louise were a blossom on the morning glory bush, showing off. Louise didn't much want to bloom. She would rather be a boy than a blooming girl. A blooming girl could no longer play in the creek in just her underwear. A blooming girl had to sit with her legs crossed.

There were other changes in Louise that summer. New realizations swarmed like long-buried locusts. She began to understand that Papa checking on a sick calf after dinner was an excuse to drink the brown juice hidden in a bottle among the hay bales. She learned that "Polly's Cow," was not her Grandmother's special pet. It was the one targeted to be butchered and its parts wrapped in white freezer paper labeled "hamburger" or "T-bone." She realized now that the fried chicken on her plate had been a live animal scratching in the yard earlier in the morning.

Louise also noticed a flaw in Grandma that year, a broken thread in an otherwise fine warm quilt. A flaw that went against the Bible.

The first morning of her visit Louise spent with Papa, pushing a wheelbarrow of salt across the pastures, tossing the granules on flat rocks for cows to lick. Bobby and Billy, the hired help, were mending a fence by the creek. They had gleaming black skin and deep voices. Louise thought they were exotic. Bobby's round face and droopy mustache reminded her of TV images she'd seen of Martin Luther King. She wanted to ask Bobby if he knew Dr. King, and why some people didn't like him, but she didn't. There was an invisible barrier, a barbed-wire fence of ideas too sensitive to touch.

When Grandmother rang the brass bell for lunch everybody met at the back porch and washed hands in water from a hose that Papa held. Black, brown, speckled and white fingers, palms and knuckles turned together in the glittering spray. When they were done Louise took a sip from the hose and scrunched her nose at the Sulphur well water, a rotten egg smell she never fully got used to.

Bobby and Billy sat on the concrete porch steps and wiped their foreheads with rags from their back pockets. Papa's yellow dogs, Franklin and Eleanor, scooted from under the house, tails wagging. Bobby bent and picked a fat tick off Franklin, crushed it with his boot.

"Can't crush a tick," Billy said. "Got to burn it."

"Looks crushed," Bobby said. "What you think Louise?"

Louise squinted at the splat of blood. "Crushed," she said. "Seed ticks you got to burn though."

Louise and Papa took off their shoes and walked sock-footed through the screened porch to the kitchen. Grandmother stood with her thin back to them in front of the stove, stirring a skillet of corn. Fried chicken and butter beans were on the table, glasses of sweet tea and china plates with roses around the rim.

Papa filled two plates and took them to Bobby and Billy. The screen door slammed as he left and whined on its hinges when he returned.

"Can't they eat with us?" Louise asked.

"No child," Grandma sat the bowl of hot corn on a potholder on the table. "They been traipsing in smelly manure all morning."

"We're smelly too," Louise said.

"Won't do no good arguing Louise," Papa said. He pinched Grandma's bottom and kissed her neck before heading to the bathroom to wash his hands with soap. Louise gave her hands a "proper cleaning," as Grandma would say, at the kitchen sink. The morning glories outside the window had closed in the heat, like children taking a nap, tiny faces hidden in their arms.

"Bobby and Billy could wash up too," Louise said.

"Those boys are fine out there," Grandma said.

Papa chuckled. "You know how I stand Polly. What's the harm?"

Grandma's face hardened. She wiped a glaze of sweat from her forehead with the hem of her apron, pulled out a chair and sat at the table with her family.

"Say grace Herman." The knuckles in Grandma's bony right hand grew pale as she gripped her fork. "And don't bring this battle to my kitchen table."

Papa mumbled his usual dinner prayer, slurring words into one giant sentence without pausing for breath. "Bless this food to our use and us to thy service and keep us mindful of the needs of others. In Jesus' name Amen."

Silver forks clicked against china. A bob-white spoke its name outside the kitchen window. Franklin sounded a feeble bark.

"Get on down from here dog," Bobby said, his voice muffled through the screen door.

Louise glanced toward the door, then back at her plate. She refused to look at Grandma.

"Don't sulk Louise," Grandma said. "Those boys are used to eating outside. Gobble every bite we set out. Trust me they're thankful."

"It's hot though," Louise said. She swallowed a mouthful of corn and pushed her chicken thigh aside. That was also new this year, losing a taste for Grandma's fried chicken.

"What about 'do unto others,' Grandma," Louise said. "*You* wouldn't want to eat on the back porch in the sun with dog slobber."

Grandma's voice sharpened.

"It's not hot Louise. It's mild June weather."

Louise felt uneasy inside, thorny like the purple thistles by the pond, like prickly pears that grew around the cow paddies in the barn lot. She'd never felt mad toward Grandma, who always let Louise have her way. Now she wanted to yell at Grandma, tip her tea glass over. She needed to get out of the kitchen. It was the blooming making her mad, showing her the stony soil of Grandma's heart, putting new thoughts in her head.

Stupid blooming, taking over Louise's body and mind. She couldn't help herself from jumping up.

"Good then," Louise said. "If it's so mild I'll take my dessert outside."

Grandma sighed and wiped a strand of grey hair behind her ear. "Go on then," she said. "Be like your Mama."

Louise picked a chocolate brownie off a tray on the counter and walked outside. Bobby and Billy sat on the top step, rose plates balanced on their knees. The dogs lapped up cooking scraps that Grandma had thrown out on the flat rock a few feet from the porch.

"I'm eating dessert with ya'll," Louise said.

"Well, have a seat," Bobby said. "You help cook this?"

"Naw, Grandma did."

"Um hum. Thought so. You learn her cooking. You'll be glad someday."

Catch yourself a fine young man you cook like this," Billy said.

Louise didn't say anything because she didn't want to catch a man. What did that mean anyway, "catch" a man? Set out traps for him like the ones Papa placed in the garden for raccoons? Or put him in a giant glass jar like a frog, with holes punched in the top for breathing and a sprig of leaves to nibble? Also, her stomach hurt from being mad at Grandma. The brownie tasted heavy in her throat. She walked down the steps and tossed the uneaten portion on the flat rock.

"I'm eating lunch out here tomorrow," Louise said.

"What's Miss Polly say about that?" Bobby asked.

Louise scrunched her shoulders. She didn't care. She'd seen something in Grandma she hadn't noticed before, something Louise didn't like. There was a flaw in Grandma that went against the Bible. Grandma had *prejudice*, a word Louise learned from Daddy.

Back in the spring Louise and Daddy had been sitting on the sofa in the living room trying to settle on a TV show. Their house-cat Tiger purred in Louise's lap and licked his scratchy tongue on her arm. Mama was in the kitchen cutting onions for a stew when Walter Cronkite came on TV talking about an important man assassinated in Memphis. Louise had heard of Martin Luther King from TV but she didn't know much about him. Daddy did though. He was mad.

"Had to be some prejudicial scumbag," Daddy mumbled. He slammed his folded newspaper against the arm of the couch, stood up and paced the floor. "Some scumbag shot Dr. King," he yelled toward the kitchen. "Come watch this, Hellen!"

Mama walked into the doorframe and told Daddy to shush, motioned toward Louise, then took a seat on the couch. She brought with her the sharp smell of onions. Quiet onion tears moistened her eyes.

"Why did he get assassinated?" Louise asked. The word was new to her, and sounded worse that "shot," or "killed" or even "murdered."

"Shush honey," Daddy said.

"What's prejudicial?"

"Shush now we're trying to listen."

When she asked again, with an impatient wine in her voice, Daddy bent down to her level, held her shoulders and looked into her brown eyes with his green ones.

"Louise, don't ever judge somebody by how they look. It's what's inside that matters, okay?"

"I know," Louise said. "I don't judge." She scratched Tiger behind the ears and focused her attention on the cat with the self-righteous knowledge of a kid. She would never judge or be a prejudicial scumbag.

If only now Louise could pick out the prejudice parts in Grandma, like she did the dark flecks of mushrooms from her stew, set them aside and keep what was good. Because mostly Grandma was wonderful.

The screen door screeched and Papa walked out.

"Finish up boys we got work in the back lot."

Bobby and Billy stacked their dishes by the door.

"Louise is trying to get you boys a seat inside," Papa said. His grin spread ear to ear.

Bobby's and Billy's eyes met.

110

"Don't worry about us Miss Louise," Bobby said. "We like it out here, long as she keeps cooking that soul food. Don't cause no trouble with Grandma Polly."

The men set out across the barn lot. One of Papa's freckled white arms lay across Bobby's black shoulder, his other arm over Billy's. Papa's laughter carried for a while but Louise couldn't make out any more conversation.

Franklin loped up the steps and licked the plates.

"Grandma wouldn't like you doing that old boy," Louise said. "You got to eat on the flat rock. We got serious eating rules around here." Franklin cocked his head. Louise stacked the dishes and took them inside.

For Louise, the fun had gone from the day.

She knew where to find Papa's brown juice. Louise climbed the straight ladder to the barn rafters, felt amongst the hay bales for the bottle and took a sip. The liquid burned her throat. She capped the bottle after three sips and sat in the rafters with a handful of fussy hens.

The brown juice made her bolder. Maybe she would tell Grandma that how you look doesn't matter. Maybe she would tell Papa she didn't want to blossom. She could be a boy better than a girl. She could hit a baseball and knew about fixing fences and feeding cows, could catch crawdads with her bare hands. She liked her overalls better than shiny boots and flower dresses her classmates wore. She didn't see the sense in eyeshadow.

Louise fell asleep in the hay and dreamed she was walking the pastures with a black boy her age, a cousin of Bobby. They caught crawdads in the creek and made a bet on who could hold on to theirs the longest. They were both good at pinching the crusty critters tight between their thumbs and forefingers. Both good at staring each other down.

"We can't stay here forever," the boy said. "We'll get ticks and chiggers."

Louise agreed. They let their craw-dads free at the count of three and headed in separate directions.

"See ya," the boy waved.

"Good-bye," Louise said. She felt incredibly sad to see the boy go.

Louise woke to the sound of her name carrying across the barn lot. The back of her neck itched from the prickly straw. It took a moment to remember where she was. How long had she slept in the hay?

"Coming Grandma!" she called as loud as she could. Before climbing down she stole three eggs, two brown and one white, from a hen's nest and lay them gently in the bib of her overalls.

The barn door eased open and Grandma stood in the bright shaft of light in her paisley house dress and clunky brown boots. Louise squeezed her eyes against the sudden brightness that put an angel glow around Grandma.

"I got these for you," Louise said, handing over the still-warm eggs as a peace offering. Grandma deposited them in the deep pockets of her dress.

"Lord, child you scared me half to death. Herman put the bull in the barn while fixing those back fences. That bull charges! You come out here without telling anybody, you could get gorged." Grandma's face was flushed pink. Worry lines showed in her creased forehead and her hair, wind-blown back, look thinner than usual.

"I'm sorry." Louise hung her head. Her eyes smarted with tears. "I didn't mean to scare you."

"Well don't do it again. We'll be careful walking back. He's over on the far side, under that clump of cedars."

Grandma picked a tobacco stick off the ground and carried it with her, as though a piece of flimsy wood could protect them against a charging bull. She and Louise walked along the fence in silence, like through a minefield, avoiding cow paddies and prickly-pear, nervously glancing toward the resting bull on the other side of the lot.

Louise took a deep breath.

"So about the eggs," she said. "I didn't know if you would want the brown ones."

Grandma stayed silent a moment then said, "I know where you are going with this young lady and I'm not discussing it."

Louise kicked a dirt clod that brought a spray of dust into the air. Grandma gave her a sharp glance.

"It's the blooming Grandma. I can't help it."

"Well, you are forming your own opinions and that is part of growing up."

"I don't want to bloom into a woman," Louise said. She broke into tears and walked faster than Grandma, three steps ahead. "I'd rather be a boy."

"If you were a boy you'd be blooming into a man," Grandma shouted. "Although they don't say blooming about boys. They say "becoming" or "developing into," but it's the same thing. And, you'd probably have to go to war. Would you want that? Do you want to go to Vietnam?"

Louise hung back and waited for Grandma. They had reached safety at the back-yard gate.

"No. I'd just like to stay me. A person ought to have a say about that."

Grandma sighed and knelt down to her granddaughter.

"I tell you what, just for today let's pretend it is last summer. You are 11. We can watch our shows and drink cokes and I won't mention a thing about sitting lady-like or being fitted for a bra. And if you want to play in the creek in your underwear, well as long as I go with you and no one sees. How does that sound? We'll slide back time for one afternoon."

Louise smiled. It was a game. The old fun Grandma was back.

"I'll fix the cokes and you turn on the TV," Louise said.

But time does not slide back. One Life to Live was pre-empted by a special newscast from Walter Cronkite. Louise brought the cold coke bottles and box of butter cookies in on a tray. She placed it on the coffee table and sat on the couch by Grandma.

Another important man had been assassinated: Robert Kennedy.

"Prejudicial scumbag," Louise mumbled. It was the only thing she could think to say. Same as what Daddy said about the other assassination. Grandma let out a gasp, glanced at Louise then pursed her lips and turned back to the TV.

"I didn't mean you," Louise said. "A prejudice scumbag probably killed him."

Grandma put her face in her hands, a closed morning glory. Louise scooted closer and put her arms around Grandma. The two sat in a wordless embrace, listening to the crackly voice of Walter Cronkite tell them what was happening as they nibbled butter cookies and sipped cokes. Grandma planted kisses and fat salt tears on top of the little girl's head while Louise slowly bloomed and time moved on.

Lisa McCormack

Lisa McCormack lives with her husband on a lake on the outskirts of Nashville, where she enjoys writing, swimming, reading, gardening and watching wildlife. She works from home as a sales director for a NY publisher. Before her sales career, and a very long time ago, she worked at The Tennessean covering stories outside Nashville. She has a bachelor's degree in journalism from Middle Tennessee State University. She has one son who lives in Denver, Co.

A Night in St. Louis
By Race McKee

It's November. I'm on my way to Washington, D.C. but all the eastern airports are socked in by a freak, early snowstorm so our plane is diverted to St. Louis. I land at Lambert International Airport in a cold, dark rain. The kind of cold that only happens in the Midwest, chilling you to the bone even before you exit the jet way.

I leave the terminal, head toward baggage claim and there she is. Her dress is the color of a clear, fall sky. It brings out her eyes...cobalt and icy, eyes that stare through to your soul. She walks with purpose. Her dress sashays, giving her the appearance of a floating angel. Blonde hair bounces as she walks. She catches my obvious stare. Our eyes lock, blue on blue, she pauses. I trip over my suitcase but catch myself before I hit the floor. Smooth is smooth, baby. She giggles. I try to rally and say, "Nothing like a trip at the end of a trip."

Weary after sixteen hours of planes, trains and automobiles (and trying to recover), I follow with, "Sorry to bother, but it's my first time at this airport. Can you point me at a cup of coffee?"

She smiles and says, "You look like you could use one."

117

I reply, "Wow, that bad, huh? If you care to join me, could you please throw a cup in my face so it'll work faster?"

With a coquettish grin she says, "My son's flight is delayed anyway, and I can use the coffee but why don't you just drink it because trust me, dousing you with it will not go with your outfit."

I perform a courtly bow and reply, "I shall respect your sense of fashion. Lead the way."

Making small talk I ask, "Where's your son flying in from? The east coast airports are a mess, it seems."

She replies, "He's a marine. He was stationed in the Pacific but rotating back to the states." With a forlorn look she says, "I haven't seen him in thirteen months. He's only here for two days and then flying back east...some mystery assignment that he doesn't know much about or can't tell me." We find a coffee joint and I realize I never caught her name. Coffee shops can help with that. We get to the counter and the barista asks, "What can I get you?"

I defer to my new friend and say, "Pick your poison."

She replies, "Grande drip, black."

A girl after my own heart. I say, "Make that two, barkeep."

The barista asks, "What name on the cup?"

She replies, "Anita."

Our barista is wearing a Led Zeppelin t-shirt and asks, "And you, sir?" I couldn't resist and say, "Whole lotta' love."

Our twenty-something barista, who's obviously an old soul, bursts out laughing and my new friend, Anita, actually snorts when she laughs. Adorable. We snag the one vacant table in the place.

Anita asks, "Where are you headed?"

I reply, "D.C. A work thing."

"What do you do?"

I say, "It's inside the Beltway, so you know it's with the government."

She says, "That's vague."

I reply, "I just met you. Mystery is not a bad thing."

"I'll grant you that," she says with a smile that would make a train take a dirt road.

I reply, "Let's just say I'm in the business of stopping bad men from doing bad things."

"Fair enough. Are you former military?"

"No," I reply, trying to deflect, "I do work with some rather remarkable military personnel though. Truth be told, one exceptional young man recently saved my life."

"Anything you can talk about?"

"I can't give you details but I was in a meeting with a couple of diplomats. One is a progressive which put him at odds with some of the local radicals, several of whom stormed our location and tried to kill him. A young marine interceded like an early version of John Wayne, took down four assailants and very likely saved three lives...including my own"

Wide-eyed she replies, "Wow...when you said you worked for the government I expected something a little more mundane."

I reply, "My job requires me to travel...and sometimes to not so nice places."

"So the mystery continues. Travel, diplomacy, bad guys. Are you a spy?"

I laugh and say, "Hardly, but if I was and told you, I'd have to kill you," and wink. "I've been told I'm good with people and keep my head about me when things get heated so I tend to get sent to places where the kettle is about to boil."

She replies, "Then I guess you do travel a lot these days. It seems like half the world is pissed-off at each other, if you'll pardon my French."

"Oh, I'm fluent in that kind of French, so no worries."

She asks with a concerned look, "Was there shooting involved with the diplomat?"

"Yes."

"Were you scared?"

I reply, "Of course, but time sort of slows down and you do what you have to do. It's been my experience the adrenaline kicks in and you get the shakes afterwards."

"What did you do?"

"It sounds like a bad movie script but I flipped over the table and drug my two guests behind it and just like the movies...the marines came in to save the day."

"That's quite a story and..." Her phone rings. She answers and says excitedly, "Michael, are you on the ground? O.K...I'm here at the airport. What gate are you at? Perfect. I'm at a coffee shop just outside of Terminal C so I'll meet you when you come out."

Bright-eyed, she turns to me and says, "I'm sorry, I have to go. My son says he's...what do you call it? 'Hitting the head' and will be here in a minute."

I reply, "If you don't mind, I'd like to tag along and meet this young man."

"It would be my pleasure, sir."

"Well, thank you, ma'am."

"Geez...Am I old enough to be a ma'am?"

In my best southern drawl I reply, "Merely a southern boy showing respect."

We make our way to the mouth of the terminal exit and a squared-away young man in jungle camouflage with eyes as blue as mine exits the concourse. I'm surprised...he even more so. He stops dead in his tracks and snaps to attention. His eyes click from his mom to me...and back...and back again. He says, "Colonel??"

I reply, "At ease, sergeant major" with a devilish grin, "I hope you don't mind but I bought your mom a cup of coffee."

The young soldier stands easy at perfect parade rest. His mother stands stunned with mouth agape. "No, s-s-sir...not at all. I'm just a little surprised to see you here...and I'm just a First Sergeant, sir."

I ask, "Do you believe in serendipity, son?

"I believe I'm beginning to, sir."

"Do you know why you were recalled to Washington?"

"No, sir. I assumed I was just being reassigned," he replied.

I reply, "Not quite. There will be a little more pomp and ceremony once we land in D.C. but since fate has brought your mother, you and I all together in St. Louis of all places, I'll give you a little preview."

I look from mother to son. Both have a look of bewilderment painted across their faces. I snap to attention and say, "Ten-hut!" Six-foot, three of chiseled marine becomes ramrod straight in the middle of the airport terminal. A small crowd starts to gather around us. I continue, "On October 15, 2018, our embassy in Manila was attacked by radical insurgents. At great risk to his own person, First Sergeant, Michael Korvin, waded through a hail of enemy fire, suppressing several insurgents and saving the life of the Philippine Foreign Minister, our American Ambassador and one very grateful marine colonel.

His exemplary courage and gallantry brings great credit to his family, his country and the Marine Corps. In recognition of your multiple acts of heroism on that day, you will receive the Silver Star and be promoted to the rank of Sergeant Major. The next time I go to war, son, I want you watching my six." I snap a crisp salute which is returned in kind. Applause is heard from our small audience as a tear rolls down his mother's cheek.

I toss my cup into a nearby trash can and say, "To hell with the coffee, Sergeant Major. Why don't we go get a plane ticket to D.C. for your mom and then get a drink worthy of a warrior?"

The sergeant beams, his mom returns the smile and he says, "Yes, sir, but I'm buying."

"The hell you are. You can buy me one after you're an E-9."

His mom grabs my arm, smiles and says, "I thought you said you weren't military?"

I reply, "I said I wasn't *Ex*-military. Geez, do I look that old?"

Race McKee

Race McKee is a published author, playwright and award-winning humorist. A former professional athlete who hails from the rural South, McKee often draws upon the world of sport or his southern lineage in applying his distinctive brand of humor.

Re-Elect the President

By Anthony J. Mohr

It was 6:30 in the morning, Friday, June 9, 1972, a week
after I'd graduated from Columbia Law School, and the
Committee to Re-Elect the President was calling to offer me a
job. I forced myself out of bed and stumbled toward the closest
telephone, in the den. Outside, the fog blocked the Santa Monica
Mountains. The Riviera Golf Course down the hill, normally
visible, was fogged in.

"Tony," said Connie Santarelli in a chipper voice. The wife
of one of President Richard Nixon's deputy attorneys general,
she was the staff member who'd interviewed me in January. "I
apologize for not calling you sooner, but you know politics. It's
been busy in Washington."

"I'm sure," I said, now fully awake.

Connie had promised to call me back well in advance of
my graduation from law school, enough time to let me make
plans, pack, move to Washington, D.C., and join the campaign.

"But," she continued, "we need you here immediately. We
have a job for you which calls for, shall we say, partisanship."

This was the phone call I'd given up on. Four years
earlier, as an undergraduate at Wesleyan, I'd interned on the

Nixon-Agnew Campaign Committee and stayed through Election Day on November 5, 1968. I could live with Nixon's politics. Thanks to their stance on the Vietnam War, I abhorred Lyndon Johnson and distrusted Hubert Humphrey, whom I was sure the Democrats would nominate. What's more, I believed there was a "new Nixon" who talked of achieving "an honorable peace" in Vietnam, rebuilding cities, and involving the young. He'd appeared on *Rowan & Martin's Laugh-In* and said, "Sock it to me." In his first term, Nixon had ended the draft and lowered the voting age to eighteen. He was almost cool.

I'd spent my 1968 internship working with several members of the campaign's leadership. I'd written press releases for Patricia Hitt, the national co-chair. I'd performed research for Robert Ellsworth, the political director, and Richard Kleindienst, who'd become deputy attorney general. At the Republican National Convention in Miami Beach, John Ehrlichman, Nixon's future domestic affairs adviser, put me in charge of the message center. I'd spent a day touring with Richard Nixon, had met him, his wife, and two daughters, and while we talked, each had looked me straight in the eye with no eagerness to move on to somebody else. High cotton for a twenty-one-year-old college kid. I'd also met the campaign chairman, John N. Mitchell, who barely said a word to me and whose handshake felt like a dead fish. I'd written my senior thesis about the campaign, and despite his politics, my faculty adviser, the former chair of Students for

Kennedy in 1960, awarded me honors. As one of the few Nixon supporters on campus, my classmates viewed me as an oddity, yet they treated me with respect. Civility still existed in politics. Even at Columbia, where in 1970 a strike shut down the law school after Nixon sent troops into Cambodia, nobody shouted at me or threatened me.

Through my senior year at Wesleyan and throughout law school, I'd had a single career goal: to work once again for Richard Nixon. I believed in him and craved the excitement of his next campaign. During our January 1972 interview, Connie had all but assured me that the Committee to Re-Elect the President (some called it CREEP) would bring me back in June. We'd talked about what I'd do—speech writing and issue research, an extension of my earlier tasks.

"If you make me an offer, I'll take it," I said. "I promise."

Then, nothing. February. March. April. May. No letter from Connie. No phone call. Disappointed, convinced that the Committee had decided against me, I accepted a clerkship with a federal judge in Los Angeles and registered to take the California bar examination.

"Let me transfer you to your new boss," Connie said. "He reports to Jeb Magruder."

I blinked. Magruder was the campaign's deputy director. The den started spinning around me, or maybe I was spinning around the den, as a warm glow suffused me and fed my elation.

So this is how you feel when dreams come true. Edward Failor came on the line. From 1963 to 1966, he'd sat on the Municipal Court of Dubuque County, Iowa. A young appointment. He'd been thirty-six in 1963.

"I'm the special assistant to the chairman for operations," Mr. Failor said. "But actually, that's a lot of bullshit. What I'm really in charge of is the negative line of the campaign." I shifted the receiver from one hand to the other as he went on. "We're going to do everything possible to cut up McGovern. Destroy his platform. Give him bad press coverage. When he talks about minorities, we go before ethnic groups and do our thing."

A nervous roll passed through me. This differed sharply from my responsibilities four years earlier. Failor continued. "I can't tell you over the telephone all the things you and I are going to do, but let's just say we're going to have a helluva lot of fun."

During the 1968 race, the campaign had maintained an "answer desk" to criticize every statement made by Hubert Humphrey and his running mate, Edmund Muskie. They'd also formed a "truth squad" of surrogate candidates to follow Humphrey around the country and counter everything he'd said minutes after he said it. The answer desk and truth squads had functioned in the open, their existence publicized. What Failor was describing verged on something secretive, edgy.

"Get on a plane, and let's get going Monday morning," Failor said.

"Well," I said, "I hadn't heard anything since January, and so I've accepted a clerkship with a federal judge."

"Forget that," Failor said. "We'll get you another federal judge."

I said, "I also signed up to take the California bar."

"We'll get you into the bar back here," Failor said.

I had trouble believing these assurances. Playing for time, I said, "Didn't National Airport shut down yesterday?" According to the news, a heavy rain was pounding the D.C. area.

"Tony," Failor said, "you'll never have another chance to work for Dick Nixon at this level. And after we win, you could be in the White House. We trust you, Tony. You come highly recommended."

Shaking, I asked, "Can I think about it over the weekend?"

Connie broke into the conversation. "If it's money," she said, "don't worry. We'll pay you fifteen hundred a month," an astounding sum for a political campaign to offer a kid fresh out of law school in 1972. She repeated the probability of a White House appointment come 1973. "Tony, call us back and say yes."

Clad in their white bathrobes, my mother and stepfather came into the den. I'd always imagined that, like the day Columbia had accepted me, they'd cheer at the news that I'd be rejoining the Nixon campaign. They didn't. As soon as I described

129

the position the committee was offering, my mother frowned. Her reaction didn't shock me. My mother had always been a Democrat. But Stan's face remained neutral, and that did surprise me, for Stan was a lifelong Republican.

"I don't know about this," Stan said, his voice barely above a whisper. He often spoke that way, odd for a man who stood six foot two and weighed almost two hundred pounds. He had a large balding head, appropriate for a businessman, it seemed to me. "It doesn't sound right."

Although something about the job description seemed wrong to me too, I suppressed my doubts and said, "But you know this is what I've wanted to do after law school." Especially after law school—three years of casebooks that weighed five pounds and statutes that rambled on forever.

"And now they want you," my mother said in a voice rich with irony. "They're waving the flag and playing the music." She raised her arm to brandish an imaginary flag, then marched in place as she broke into a mocking da dah, da-da-da, da-da-dah cadence of John Philip Sousa's "Stars and Stripes Forever." She may have been fifty-six, but with her clear complexion, solid limbs, strong chin, and lively blue eyes, my mother still looked youthful and pretty. A moment later she froze, stared at me, and said, "You study for the bar." My mother always wanted a lawyer for a son.

"Mom, the timing is perfect," I said, and before I could add anything more, the phone rang.

Connie again.

"Tony," she said, "National Airport is open. Come on back. I can't stress enough how much this opportunity will mean to you. We need you, Tony." As she spoke, I stared out the bay window at what people called Southern California's June gloom. Droplets of water clung to the glass.

"I just need to—think," I said. I knew I was begging and disliked myself for doing so.

"We can take care of everything," Connie said.

"The job doesn't sound right," Stan repeated after I hung up. "They can't wave a hand and get you into the bar."

Stan had tapped into a truth I wanted to ignore. No president could whisk me into the bar without taking the examination. I wanted to attribute Failor's promises to puffery, his eagerness to recruit me. I started to say that, but Stan fixed me with the same expression he'd assumed at dinner several years earlier, when he said he'd failed to land an order for one of the business machines his company manufactured because he'd refused to pay a bribe.

Since 1950, the year Stan had moved to California, he'd supported Richard Nixon. He'd given him money. Stan and Nixon shared the same insurance broker, Republican State Chairman V. John Krehbiel, a man with a cherubic persona, every feature in

131

Waspish symmetry. Nixon would name Krehbiel ambassador to Finland. In 1969, Nixon had approached Stan to serve in his administration, but ever the self-employed entrepreneur, Stan said no.

"Are you sure you want to do this?" Stan asked me a little while later as the three of us sat down for breakfast.

My mother poured herself a cup of coffee. "Shouldn't you get the bar exam out of the way?"

I let my scrambled eggs grow cold and barely touched the sausages my mother had cooked—crisp, golden brown, the way I liked them.

Stan said, "I don't understand why he has to spend so much time tearing apart George McGovern."

I told them what I'd learned from my friends in the 1968 campaign: "Nixon wants a landslide." A thumping victory, the most overwhelming presidential victory in history.

"All he needs to do is win," my mother said.

Stan left the table. It was time for him to get dressed and leave for work. "We need to talk more about this tonight," he said, moving his hands up and down as he talked, a tic he displayed whenever he felt strongly about something.

The remainder of the morning was a blur; my bar review materials, words on a page. During lunch, I picked at my chicken salad sandwich and crunched on potato chips.

"We'll support whatever you want to do," my mother said.

Almost all of my law school classmates were headed for Wall Street law firms, typical for Columbia. I'd learned enough about those places to know the work could bore without end, drafting indenture agreements, reading subordination clauses. With Richard Nixon, I'd break free from all that. No interrogatories. No dreary depositions. No proofreading through the night at the financial printers. I was bound for the commanding heights with an office down the hall from my commander in chief.

And once Nixon left office in 1976, I'd own that magical label: a Washington insider. Who knew where I'd land? A subcabinet post if another Republican won? A judgeship, like Ed Failor? Was this job offer such a bad thing? All I had to do was learn how to slash and burn. Wasn't that part of politics? At four o'clock Friday afternoon, the sun emerged. I moved my bar review materials to a table in the den, but still didn't read them.

"I'll bet you could work in the administration after your clerkship," Stan said over dinner, which I wasn't eating.

"I doubt it," I said, then stammered, "If I turn them down, I'll have to practice law."

"Is that so terrible?" my mother asked.

"Yes it is," I blurted out, louder than I should have. "I'd rather dig ditches."

"Tony, this is a decision you're going to have to make for yourself," Stan said calmly.

I finished the apple pie my mother had made for dessert. My mother, who loved me unconditionally, was indulging me with comfort food while I studied for the bar exam.

My parents and I talked all weekend. They watched me wander around the backyard. They asked where I'd live in D.C. My mother offered to pick out the clothes I'd take should I leave come Monday. Stan wondered how my judge would react when I broke my promise to clerk for him. My mother wondered if, at the end of the campaign, I'd be willing to take time off to study for the bar instead of joining the White House staff. She asked, "Do you think you'll ever become a lawyer?"

In the den early Sunday evening, my mother put another question to me. "How are you going to feel about smearing a person?"

My mother was right. I was a sensitive kid, not a barracuda. Despite what Failor said, I wasn't sure I'd have a lot of fun. I wished they'd offered me my former job. Stan and my mother sat quietly while I fought back tears. By then they were out of words except for phrases like "We love you" and "We know you'll do the right thing."

Monday morning, I called to break the promise I'd made to Connie, as well as to myself. "I've thought about it and my commitment to the judge. It hurts, Connie, but I have to say no."

"You're making a mistake, Tony," Ms. Santarelli said.

I asked, "Can we get in touch at the end of my clerkship?"

"Maybe," Ms. Santarelli said in a neutral tone of voice.

***

For the rest of the summer, I followed the campaign with the ache of an outsider, face pressed against the glass, peering in at a party. Each morning at the bar review class, surrounded by people who'd never have the opportunity I'd just wasted, I felt like a neurotic who feared success. How many people kill their dreams the moment they turn real?

I searched the press for any mention of Ed Failor and found none until September, at the start of my clerkship, when *Life Magazine* ran an article titled "Confidence, With a Little Paranoia." The reporter quoted Failor as saying he was "'...just a country boy from Iowa doing God's work in the vineyards.'" But I knew what Ed was doing in the shadows—activities more rousing than contracts and torts.

Life Magazine's writer caught Failor's true function: to run "...basically an attack line." Then the reporter cited a front page of the Washington Post in which the three top stories criticized McGovern. Failor "orchestrate[d]" the methods by which Republican spokesmen would "flail at McGovern." The reporter went on to wonder whether Failor, for instance, had encouraged "Senator Robert Dole's charge that the McGovern organization had violated the contribution reporting law seven times? Failor looks shocked. 'I can't get into that.' He grins through some cheerful wrangling about his reticence, which he admits. 'That's why they have me up here on the eighth floor.'" I read the article several times, which was several times more than I'd read, three months earlier, a small piece about several men who'd been arrested for breaking into the headquarters of the Democratic National Committee. I'd considered the incident a political hiccup, and it didn't stop me from voting for Nixon on November 7, 1972.

That arrest mushroomed into Watergate.

As Richard Nixon often said before answering a question, "Let me make one thing perfectly clear." To my knowledge, Edward Failor was not prosecuted in connection with Watergate. He denied any participation in anything related to it. That may be, but he nudged up against at least two criminals from the scandal, Magruder and Charles Colson. The FBI interviewed Failor in May 1973, and according to their report, "It was Mr. Failor's position to interface with Mr. Charles Colson of the White House regarding strategy matters of the upcoming Republican Presidential campaign, and as such he would hold daily meetings with Mr. Colson..."

Failor didn't see Colson alone. At least one report at the time confirmed that Failor belonged to a "mysterious attack group of political hatchet men" who met daily at 9:15 a.m. at the White House to "fog over" Watergate and pound George

McGovern. So impressed was Jeb Magruder that he gave Failor and the others cuff links lettered 9:15.

Colson pleaded guilty to obstruction of justice and served seven months in Alabama's Maxwell Prison. While there, Colson claims he found God. Magruder pleaded guilty to a one-count indictment of conspiracy to obstruct justice, defraud the United States, and illegally eavesdrop on the Democratic National Committee. Like Colson, Magruder says he found God in federal prison.

Exactly what Failor did, I never learned beyond the FBI report, but he got his reward: head of the Department of Commerce's Social and Economic Statistics Administration, an agency with a hundred-million-dollar budget and the Census under his control. Why did he end up there? The press speculated that Nixon expected Failor to manipulate figures to make the economy look "rosy." Did he? I have no idea. Would Failor have taken me along as his deputy and asked me to lie with statistics? I'll never know, but I do know that I got a C in algebra and a C in trigonometry. I also know Watergate killed my respect for Richard Nixon.

Had I joined CREEP, would I now be the author of a best-selling memoir? Would I, too, have found God in a federal prison? Until Watergate, most law school curricula, including mine, didn't stress legal ethics. Now they do. I'd like to think my parents' morals would have prevailed over the White House, but one thing I'm sure about: the chances are excellent the FBI would have interviewed me at length, as they did Ed Failor, and like Ed Failor's interview report, mine would have entered the public record, there to dog me forever.

Since 1994, I've sat as a judge, first on the Los Angeles Municipal Court and now on the Los Angeles Superior Court. I'm sure that even a near miss with Watergate would have prevented Governor Pete Wilson from appointing me.

That painful June weekend gave me practice in making hard choices, which from time to time judges must do. A sense of fulfillment comes in each time I make a ruling I think is right. Still, the bench can never offer the bracing air of a campaign, the lift of a White House job, or the thrill of strategizing on a national scale. I never do that now. Judges watch passively while lawyers and clients make their moves. Following a verdict, lawyers and clients celebrate—or mope. We judges just say, "Next case." At least I've received a consolation prize for my quiet life: the freedom to follow the law.

Anthony J. Mohr

Anthony J. Mohr's work has appeared in, among other places, Commonweal, DIAGRAM, Eclectica, Hippocampus Magazine, North Dakota Quarterly, The Saint Ann's Review, and ZYZZYVA. He has been anthologized in California Prose Directory (2013), Golden State 2017, and two volumes of Chicken Soup for the Soul. A holder of five Pushcart Prize nominations, he received honorable mention in Sequestrum's 2016 Editor's Reprint Award and is an associate editor of Evening Street Review. Once upon a time, he was a member of the LA Connection, an improv theater group. Currently he lives in Los Angeles with his wife Beverly, four birds, and two Lhasa Apsos.

The Teacher

By I. M. Merckel

Everyone loves summer. Sunny days, gentle nights, warm temperatures. Plenty of activities, and the time to do them. No shoveling snow, raking leaves, or bundling up. Yes, everyone loves summer... except me.

I travel for a living. Every week I'm at an airport, lugging a bag, standing in a security line, undergoing its indignities, and putting up with the other conditions that make flying today about as enjoyable as rowing in a Roman galley. When an occupation requires face to face meetings, the assigned territory is too vast to drive, and other transportation options are not reasonably available, travel by air is the only choice.

With the current attitude exhibited by an airline industry seeking to minimize passenger convenience and contentment, flying at times can resemble navigating the various stages of hell described in Dante's *Inferno.* As the standard of travel falls below those adhered to by the local Animal Humane Society, the travel experience becomes memorable for all the wrong reasons. Yet those conditions, hardly acceptable in other seasons, resemble a tropical oasis when compared to the summer, as family travel takes over the industry. It is then that airline discomfort receives a dose of steroids, as family vacations assure full planes, the kicking of the back of your seat by the bored child, parental meltdowns while trying to control sibling arguments, and seeking remedies to deal with the assorted sundry of other situations which arise at thirty thousand feet.

Traveling for a living, I yearn for the times when flying was something I looked forward to, where the airplane seat had some semblance to body shape and needs, and the airlines believed service was included in the price of a ticket. The good times are when children are in school so families remain at home, for it is then that a chance arises to sit beside an empty seat, and perhaps, if the stars align, to win the lottery and get a blessed empty row. Sometimes I feel like the bad golfer who swears he's giving up the game, but on the verge of breaking his clubs, hits the perfect shot, deciding to stay with the sport a little longer. By necessity, I keep flying due to a lack of other options. At the point of desperation, swearing I will never fly again, I encounter rare good fortune in the form of a little less discomfort that keeps me returning. Yet the dream remains about how nice it would be to have a desk job, sell cars, or any other occupation not necessitating air travel.

It was a typical summer travel day. I arrived early and sat waiting for the "call to the gate" by the ticket agent. Amidst the sounds of screaming children being ignored by parents and scenes of hyperactive youngsters holding Junior Olympic competitions in the concourse, I spied approaching me a tall, thin, black man, about my age. He was pushing a wheelchair occupied by a young boy. The child appeared to be about ten years old, razor thin, with closely shaved hair, head lolling from side to side, arms atwitter in constant motion. I was sitting in a vertical three-seat endcap that adjoined two long horizontal rows, the other two seats in my endcap being vacant. Watching them approach, it appeared their destination was the available seats next to me. I am not a religious man, but under the circumstances then present, I resorted to the assistance of a Higher Power to direct them to other available accommodations. Like most of my prayers, my request went unanswered. My endcap was where the man chose to sit, faced by the boy in the wheelchair.

The reader might be outraged that I would feel such things. To respond, I don't see myself as a callous person, or one who lacks empathy for my fellow man. Yet, despite the statutes passed by my government dictating how I must think and act when dealing with the less fortunate, when I see someone who is obviously struggling with an impairment, my first inclination, despite the threat of punishment for violating one of the aforesaid laws, is to avoid that person. You see, I have a deeply held feeling that what they suffer from is transmittable, as illogical or terrible as that might sound, and since I am ignorant of any known remedy for such human ailments, I must deal with this unease. My first thought is to improve the plight of that less fortunate fellow by moving elsewhere and offering my seat. That might temporarily resolve my issues, but I cannot hide from my selfish motives, directed not at assisting that person, but relieving my own concerns; something that requires dealing with the guilt that follows.

On this occasion, giving up my seat was not an option, as there remained an empty position between us, and the subjects had already selected where they would sit. That left me with two other choices. I could still get up and move or remain in place. The former concerned me since they could view this as insulting or being intolerant. That reflected poorly on me, something I did not want to face, although neither the man nor boy knew me, and the odds weren't high that our paths would cross again. But I know myself. I didn't want strangers thinking poorly of me, regardless of how base my actions, for I feared that if I walked away a flashing neon arrow would descend from the heavens and point me out as a bad person — an opinion I, at times, knew was true, but which fact I did not want shared. The second option, the least desirable path, was to remain in place, act as if nothing was different, all the time praying that I would be called to the departure gate early. Since I am a practical person, the second option was the one I selected, not by choice, but by elimination.

Out of the corner of my eye, my hearing attuned, I followed the discourse between the man and his ward. The child could communicate, his speech interspersed with grunts, groans, indecipherable utterances, and hand gestures. What emanated from him was incomprehensible to me, but, evidently was as clear as could be to his companion. The man's responses were prompt and concise, spoken in the King's English, as if all that the child uttered was totally understandable to everyone. It was like eavesdropping on the initial conversation between Henry Higgins and Eliza Doolittle, the protagonists in *My Fair Lady*. When dribble appeared at the edge of the child's mouth, the man would lean over, carefully wipe it, the boy would laugh, mumble something, and their conversation would resume. When something at the gate would seize the child's attention, suspending his communication as he stared through semi-glazed eyes, the man would follow his glance. Whatever was viewed would then become the subject of the next round of exchanges. When the child winced, the man would reseat him in a different position, enlisting a soft coo or a smile from the wheelchair inhabitant. Even when the child issued a sharp loud cry, the man's response was always to lean forward, make some adjustment, and bring the child back from the edge of misery.

I watched, without staring, and listened to them for a good half-hour, as best I could, given their strange conversation. In that time, I gleaned that the man was the uncle of the boy, that only the youngster was flying, and the boy was to be met at the end of his journey by his mother. I couldn't tell whether he lived with the uncle, was visiting him, or was in town for treatment for his condition. The answer would have little importance other than to placate my curiosity. When the pre-flight announcement from the gate across from us was made, the man got up, nodded at me in parting, and wheeled the boy across to that area for early boarding. From the departure destination signs I saw the boy was going either to Omaha or parts east. I hoped it was Omaha, for to have the little guy make flight connections would be a significant task.

They stood near the gangway door, appearing to converse in their special language. Then, as boarding was about to begin, the man bent over, embraced the smiling child, who returned the hug. The boy was then wheeled down the tunnel by an attendant. As the uncle watched, the attendant, apparently familiar with the couple, stopped and turned the wheelchair at the bend in the gangway to allow the child to look back and wave, as best he could. This was met by the uncle blowing him a kiss and saying, "See you soon." As the child disappeared, the uncle slowly turned, wiped his eyes, and left the terminal.

With the departure of the two, my life returned to normal. My flight was called, I did what I had to do to survive the trip, returning a few days later when my week's work was done. Another set of meetings crossed off the calendar.

The following week found me back at the airport, doing what I always did at the beginning of my trips — awaiting my departure, eyeing who I would be flying with, contemplating how I was going to get what I perceived I needed to make the flight palatable. My thoughts normally center on air travel deficiencies that become apparent to even the first-time flyer. Will I be able to secure overhead space for storage? Who will occupy the area around me? Will they be glib, speaking at the volume level of a public address system? Do they view their laptop computer as a third appendage, feeding their addiction to electronic games that emit repetitive beeps and sounds, or the clicking and vibrations caused by their dedication to composing the great American novel, or the job memo that will save their company? Will their bladder capacity equal that of a hummingbird's, so I spend more time getting out of my seat than sitting in it? Those, while bad, do not equal the worst possibilities, like having a lap child going through stages of colic, or a service dog the size of an African termite mound. Those conditions, if they arise, must be endured while being stuffed into an area too small for a six-year-old.

While not an exhaustive list, they represent many conditions that I have been required to endure. Combine this with the knowledge that those obstacles may reoccur following a sprint through airports to make connections, and you have sown the seeds for a mental breakdown.

To demonstrate how perverted my thinking can become, I sometimes focus my attention on determining the flight miles the trip adds to my rewards travel card. Some might envy my cumulative balance, but that only provides me the opportunity to occasionally fly for free in the undesirable conditions previously described. It's like eating nine bad meals on a restaurant card to qualify for a free tenth bad meal.

This time was different. My mind kept returning to the man and the child, for there was something about them that I could not shake. Traveling permits me to view all types of relationships, but none that matched what I had seen. I'm observant, but not perceptive, so I hadn't grasped the meaning of what I had witnessed. It was intriguing, unique, and touching, yet its lesson lay beyond me.

As happens periodically, airline routings change, and this time I was in luck. My flight required no connections, going directly to my destination. That didn't happen often. A good sign. But that didn't ameliorate the remainder of my flying fears. From the look of those waiting, this was going to be another crowded flight, kicking my travelling self-survival techniques into overdrive as I contemplated the odds of what could go wrong. Another day at the office.

My good fortune continued as the crew made ready to close the hatch door. There remained unoccupied the middle seat next to me. In thirty seconds it would be free for the trip, providing sought after additional space. My heart leaped with joy at this bounty. While planning my celebration, a last-minute passenger rushed in. *No, no, don't let him be assigned this seat.* I looked down at the floor, believing that if I concentrated on the stained, threadbare, floor covering, I would render the open seat invisible. But my ruse failed, for a pair of legs came into view and stopped at my row.

"Excuse me," said the legs in a strangely familiar voice. "Can I pass, please?"

With heavy heart I unbuckled my seat belt, slowly rose, and came face to face with the new occupant, the black man from the week before. My eyes widened, as did his, as we both recalled the other.

"We sat out there last week before my flight," I stammered, forgetting that I needed to move so he could sit.

"We did," he responded, and then gestured that I needed to allow him passage.

"Sorry," was my reply as I moved out of the way, providing him access to his cramped travelling area.

He buckled in. "Man, just made it. Agent sent me to the wrong gate. I told him this was my flight, but he said it'd been changed. Turned out I was right." With that he chuckled.

Had that been me I would have been livid, taking names. But he handled it in stride.

"Not the greatest fit," I said, gesturing about the seat. "Makes you feel like a sardine."

"Yeah, but it beats walking," he said with a smile. "And unlike a sardine, I'm not dead or covered in oil. What's a couple hours out of my life, anyway?"

I knew where our conversation would go. No matter what I related was wrong in my life — the job, the plane, everyday aggravations — his comeback was predictable, downplaying and making light of his similar trials. In our different approaches we were like the moon, me the dark side, he the light, and yet, there was nothing condescending or patronizing in his comments. We were just two people who viewed things differently. He shared his opinions without seeking accord with his point of view. He was always hopeful; I was consistently doubtful.

I learned about him, about the boy, and some of their history. He was a production line supervisor for a local manufacturer. For twenty years he showed up at the same time, at the same place, to do the same job. I realized I would hate to be stuck in such a routine.

The boy was his nephew, afflicted by an incurable, non-fatal, not contagious condition. He wouldn't get better physically but was in a program working to develop skills he could perform. The boy lived in Omaha with his mother, a single parent, the man's stepsister. The boy either visited him, or he the boy, at least once a month.

"Gives her a break and gives me a chance to be with him," he said.

The more we talked, the more I envied his attitude — the calm, the peace, and the acceptance that he possessed. He shared stories of the two of them together, the good times, happy times, special times. According to him, when they were with each other, there was only laughter, adventure, and fun.

"We can't do everything others can, nor can we do many things with others, but we can do plenty with each other, and enjoy what we do. It's great when we're together."

I compared the frustrations, the ups and downs, of my own life, mostly the lows for that's what I usually concentrated on. They stood in stark contrast to the stories he shared of his world. Where I saw bad, he saw good. Where I felt cold, he felt warmth. What I struggled with, he viewed as growth opportunities. He would nod his head in commiseration but never confronted or lectured. I was provided the courtesy of his audience as I purged my resentments.

I wanted our flight to continue, that we never land, a first for me. But all things end, and this flight touched down on time. I collected my things from the overhead bin. We stood in the aisle waiting for the doors to open, me to do my job, he to make his connection to Omaha. We exchanged names, something we hadn't previously provided during our conversation, shook hands, and wished each other well. I knew that unless our flight paths crossed in the future, this would be our last meeting. I felt a loss.

"I wish I had your attitude towards things," I told him enviously, seeking to continue our discussion. "You're really upbeat on life. Nothing phases you."

"Well," he said, "I'm always learning. Life is what it is. I view it as good; what others make of it is up to them. How you see it, you live it. I don't want to waste my time worrying. I take it as it comes."

The door to the plane opened and the disembarkation process began.

"Just curious," I asked. "Where'd you learn to be like that?"

"From a great teacher. Taught me a lot."

"Learn that in High School?"

"Nah."

"College?"

"No, never attended college."

"Then who might the teacher be, if I'm not prying?"

He looked at me smiling, not judging, just wistful.

"My nephew," he said. "Best teacher I ever had. I learn things from him whenever we're together."

With that, he patted my shoulder, turned and walked off the plane.

I. M. Merckel

I. M. Merckel is a retired real estate attorney. Born in Los Angeles, he has a B.A. from the University of Arizona and a J.D. from Washington University in St. Louis. He practiced law in Missouri beginning in 1971, after leaving military service, and in 2011 from New Mexico, where he and his wife Joan now reside. He has three sons, two of whom are published authors. During his career he wrote legal documents and briefs. He is now writing fiction, although some may suggest his prior legal work provides examples of fictional composition. He has published other short stories and memoir pieces, and is completing his first novel. His pen name is in remembrance of his father whose nickname for him was Merckel.

Life and Death in Vietnam

By Lt. Col. Robert B. Robeson, USA (Ret)

"It is well that war is so terrible, or we should get too fond of it."--General Robert E. Lee, on seeing a Federal charge repulsed at Fredericksburg (December 1862).[1]

I'll never forget my first corpse encountered in combat during the Vietnam War. I was a "Dust Off," medical evacuation helicopter pilot and captain assigned to the 236th Medical Detachment (Helicopter Ambulance) stationed at Red Beach in Da Nang, South Vietnam from July 1969 to July 1970.

Dust Off was the radio call sign used by U.S. Army Medical Service Corps crews that flew unarmed helicopters to evacuate wounded and dead civilians and soldiers from both sides of the action. We routinely flew into shooting situations, both day and night, in all weather conditions and terrain. This name originated early in the war. Most people believe this call sign originated from the dust our helicopters stirred up when we were landing. It's actually an acronym that stands for Dedicated, Unhesitating Service To Our Fighting Forces. The Dust Off name stuck for the rest of this conflict.[2]

The majority of our medical missions were the stuff of melodramas. From day one, as a rookie "peter pilot," combat dredged up enough death and drama to gag a grave robber or horror movie villain.

My maiden medevac mission occurred in late July 1969. It was for an allied "ROK," Republic of Korea Marine who'd been shot in the chest in a filthy rice paddy fertilized with human excrement about ten miles south of Da Nang.

As our aircraft commander hovered close to the edge of an earthen dike, where this casualty had been shot, our rotor blades whipped the murky paddy water into a brownish froth. It was my first glimpse of what a sucking-chest wound looked like up close and personal.

His infantry comrades carried him to the door of our cargo compartment and our medic and crew chief pulled him aboard the aircraft. I surmised by the grayish color of his facial features and his obvious breathing difficulties that we were about to lose him. As we lifted off and flew toward the 95th Evacuation Hospital, located on China Beach alongside the South China Sea in Da Nang, our medic confirmed my observation.

"Sir, we just lost him. He didn't make it."

It was the first murder I'd ever witnessed, but there would be hundreds of others that would follow in succeeding weeks and months. These terminal patients would be victimized by assorted bullets, bombs and booby traps directed at "to whom it may concern" in this intense conflict.

Flying an unarmed helicopter into violent confrontations has a way of shoving a pilot out onto the high wire where precarious flying does its balancing act. It's like putting a mouse in the ring with an elephant. Sooner or later, that mouse is going to get stepped on no matter how brave and illusive it thinks it is. Perhaps that's why Dust Off losses to hostile fire were 3.3 times that of all other forms of helicopter missions in Vietnam.[3]

Life in combat was contradictory. It was bloody and messy. It could also be stupid and nerve-wracking, and it was always dangerous to the max. During my missions, with their tense emotional and physical dilemmas, I soon recognized that everything I thought I could control was like attempting to tuck a porcupine into bed.

I learned how to live with what *is* during war, not what I *wanted* it to be. It's OK and reasonable to be frightened when you're consistently being targeted and shot at. Fear is good because it makes every sense sharper. Your mind works faster and better. Nothing is wrong with fear unless it rules a person. Yet it was always apparent that combat still involved the most brutal of murders whether they were wrapped and sanctified in a nation's flag or not.

In Vietnam, the most common slang word used for death was "wasted." This was an accurate and appropriate choice of words. We learned in a hurry that "buying the farm" in combat was different from its meaning back in Iowa. To experience war, and look it in the eye, is to acknowledge that there is still madness in the world even when the cause may be perceived as just.

For our flight crews there was the victory of endurance, the prize of persistence, and the triumph of tenacity if our patients survived as we carried out our missions. In my year in Vietnam, all that our crewmembers and troops could count on were each other. We had a close bond. We provided wounded American troops, allied soldiers, and Vietnamese civilians hope, safety and were often their only way out of critical and dangerous circumstances. Those on the ground would do anything to cover us and I never met a Dust Off pilot who wouldn't risk a bird or a crew for them, regardless of the situation.

Saving everyone we went after was always our goal. I wish I could say that all those we were able to evacuate did survive, but war isn't a fairy tale. The final ending was not a happy one for millions of soldiers and civilians on both sides of the devastating action. For so many, war ate up their lives before they barely had an opportunity to live them.

In previous American conflicts, a significant percentage of patients didn't survive because helicopter support was not available and medical assistance arrived too late. Time, as the saying goes, is not only money but also equates to life and death when seriously wounded in combat.

In my year of Dust Off flying, I flew 987 missions and helped evacuate over 2,500 patients. This often meant risking my crews and aircraft to evacuate captured and wounded enemy soldiers from under the fire of their own comrades. Seven of my helicopters were shot up by enemy fire and I was shot down twice. Not only have I read the combat book, I've also played a supporting role in the subsequent movie being filmed on location. All of our crews flew for others. We flew to make a difference and to provide light to those who were momentarily lost and hurting in the darkness of battle. We offered our aircraft as a refuge for our patients, some of whom were destined to live a long time and others mere moments. It's true, combat *does* provide a strong sensory experience with otherworld sights, sounds and smells. It also made a vivid impression in my mind that all life is fragile. For many of the participants, this armed conflict became their lifetime.

It didn't take long to understand that war is emotionally, psychologically, physically and spiritually disturbing. It was a world of creative cruelty, like being invited to a suicide you didn't want to commit. Intense combat action continually reminded me that it probably wasn't supposed to make sense to the participants. Combat is murder on demand...and the demand was heavy. It was the end of innocence for all of the young soldiers on both sides and the civilian Vietnamese children who were often wounded during firefights.

During those hectic days of 1969-1970, helicopters in Vietnam seemed to fall out of the sky like fat poisoned birds, a hundred times a day. In April of 1970, two months after I'd been promoted to detachment commander, our unit had sixteen aircraft shot up or shot down between thirteen pilots. We went through our authorized inventory of six birds nearly three times in thirty days.

The constant tension, death and destruction on all sides created perpetual chopper anxiety and often temporary fear. This, and a continuous lack of sleep when the action was heavy-- we were often in the air ten or more hours a day--would tear huge chunks of energy from weary bodies and minds. None of it ever left us alone. Soldiers and civilians, alike, died in staggering numbers. Fighting in war is a universal experience but admission is never free.

Each mission demanded determined decisions by the aircraft commander. These instantaneous human judgments provided either extended existence or a dramatic demise for patients and crewmembers. On the worst days, I didn't expect to survive, but I kept at it. It constantly forced me to sift through the chaos of my daily existence for some semblance of order, stability and rationality. The apparent futility of it all was a persistent weight on my mind. For every patient I evacuated, there might be others I could never get to or help in time. I was constantly forced to confront invisible forces that I didn't have the power to change or overcome. Death became matter-of-fact, even routine, and it's something I couldn't run away from.

Many circumstances in war challenged me and created substantial fear, that could never be displayed to crewmembers. All I could do was face the constant challenges, say a prayer, and allow my training, experience and "guts" to kick-in. I couldn't expect an explanation about gross wounds or deaths that constantly surround soldiers in war or about devastating combat actions that occurred. A myriad of dangerous things occur in this twilight zone. They just happen. I was forced to accept them as facts of life. What follows are a few examples of Dust Off missions, that I was involved in.

In a two-and-one-half-day period, from August 20-22 in 1969, our crew evacuated 150 wounded Americans from the infamous Hiep Duc Valley approximately 32 miles southwest of Da Nang. We flew 42 missions, fifteen of them were "insecure." This meant that our ground troops couldn't guarantee the safety of the jungle landing zones (lz), some of which weren't much wider than our rotor blades. The enemy was usually in close contact and surrounding the landing areas or our ground troops were low on ammunition and couldn't provide sufficient covering fire.

On a majority of these insecure missions, helicopter gunships weren't readily available to cover our unarmed aircraft because there was too much action requiring their services in other parts of the battleground. Our only alternative was to go in alone, since most of the wounded wouldn't have survived if we'd wasted time waiting for gunships to arrive.

During the morning of August 21st, our UH-1H ("Huey") was shot up by enemy AK-47 rifle fire while exiting another insecure landing zone. One of our three patients was wounded for the second time. A burst of fire ripped into a can of hydraulic fluid our crew chief kept under my armored seat, spraying it onto my Nomex flight pants. Another round locked me in my shoulder harness when it clipped a wire on the unlocking device attached to the left side of my seat. We deposited our patients at the LZ Baldy aid station, 25 miles south of Da Nang, while another bird was being flown out for our use from our unit headquarters in Da Nang.

Less than 24 hours later--August 22nd--we were shot up for the second time on another insecure mission while evacuating an infantry staff sergeant who'd been shot in the back and leg. SP5 John Seebeth, our flight medic, was wounded in the throat during our 120-knot tactical approach into that jungle location. An AK-47 round tore out his larynx. Two of our three radios were also shot out and there were an assortment of bullet holes above my head in the cockpit and throughout the rest of the aircraft.

In the aid station at Baldy, I held John's legs while an Army doctor performed a tracheotomy without anesthesia. John was suffocating because the wound had swollen so fast, cutting off his oxygen. Fortunately, he somehow survived but had to endure a dozen follow-up surgeries...one of which gave him back a voice. But it wouldn't be the one we were familiar with. What I learned in those traumatic days was you never know how strong you are until that moment when you have to be. The sight of dead bodies stacked in piles on our cargo compartment deck have created scars and ragged holes in my heart, soul and psyche. For a long time, these traumatic scenes wouldn't allow me to easily convey the emotions and pain buried deep within unless it was to another veteran who had also been there.

During the night of August 20, 1969, before John was wounded, our crew had landed on Million Dollar Hill (Hill 102) three times. It received this name because a million dollars' worth of helicopters had been shot down there in one day. We evacuated three full loads of wounded American infantrymen who'd been ambushed by the North Vietnamese Army.

Thirty-two years later, due to a book titled *Fighting Back*, I discovered that the next to the last patient on that third flight at 2:00 a.m. had been an M-79 grenadier named Rocky Bleier. It was his memoir. He'd been wounded in both legs. Bleier was a

161

professional football player for the National Football League (NFL) Pittsburgh Steelers. Over the course of two years, he recovered from his wounds including a foot that nearly required amputation. Bleier became a starting halfback on the Steeler teams that won NFL Super Bowls in 1974, 1975, 1978, and 1979. I never knew whose life I would step into or who would step into mine on a mission.

On September 13, 1969, two days before my 27th birthday, I was shot down for the first time near LZ Ross. The following Christmas morning, I was shot down for the second time while making an attempt to evacuate nine wounded South Vietnamese soldiers from an outpost the Viet Cong had attacked and surrounded during a supposed ceasefire agreement signed by both sides in Paris, France. This occurred on Barrier Island, 20 miles south of Da Nang.

We took 19 "hits." Six of them were in one fuel cell, five in the cockpit and the rest in the cargo compartment. No one was hit, although one of our crew chief's boots was kicked-up by a machine gun round that made a nipple in the deck where his foot had been. Thirty minutes later, I commandeered another aircraft and we went back to successfully complete this mission in two additional attempts...again under heavy enemy fire.

In January of 1970, while evacuating seven wounded American infantrymen who'd stumbled into a booby-trapped mine field, I unknowingly placed our left skid on two mines. One was estimated to be a 250-pound anti-tank mine. Neither of them detonated. A week later, at our unit headquarters at Red Beach, an infantry first lieutenant drove over 30 miles in an open jeep to thank and inform me of this, otherwise, I wouldn't have known how close we came to being annihilated. They discovered these mines after we took off and placed C-4 plastic explosives around them. Then they blew them in place. He told me, "the top of the hill disappeared when they were blown."

During moments after battles on remote artillery bases, there would be enemy bodies strewn around the field of battle when we arrived to evacuate wounded survivors. Sometimes we landed at night in the middle of firefights featuring enemy mortars, AK-47s, flame throwers, rocket-propelled grenades and satchel charges. It was always a surreal experience.

Everywhere we went, there would be an acrid odor of decaying flesh that was often combined with the overpowering stench of gas gangrene, vomit, feces, urine, blood, gunpowder and napalm that permanently etched themselves into our weary brains. Eighteen, nineteen and twenty-year-old crew members became accustomed to it like all the rest of us. It was merely a fact of life in that type of confrontational environment.

Recalling life in combat can stir the ashes of ancient memory. Some of the things we were forced to witness and experience would be unfit for reading about even in a dark and dank dungeon by candlelight. The truth was, we were all studying war at the same institution. But if you were "smoked," "offed," "zapped," "wasted" or "greased," you couldn't graduate. The stories about the Vietnam War have gotten old and so have those of us, still around, who were there. Since then, even decades later, I've awakened too many times from nightmares when someone I've never met is once again in the process of blowing me out of the sky. I'll be shaking and sweating. Most combat veterans have experienced these universal "dark nights of the soul." They have become fractured moments that often stalk my seared soul in living color. The battle scenes can still seem as loud as a concert orchestra in maximum *fortissimo* and command my attention in macabre reruns. "Flashback" moments still occur and can make sleep unsafe.

Remembering those brave young men and women in war are as valid to me, at 76, as memories of riding with no-hands on a bicycle for the first time. They remind me of a Russian proverb about the hammer. It can shatter glass or it can forge steel. The hammer of life is similar. Whether like glass we shatter or like steel we are forged depends on what we are made of. The soldiers I knew, observed and flew with were made of the finest steel.

SP5 Delmar Pickett, one of our flight medics, was one of these soldiers. He passed away a few years ago in Wichita, Kansas. Fortunately, before his death, we were able to exchange letters and I told him how much I appreciated what he'd done in

Vietnam to help others. He'd earned five Purple Hearts, two Distinguished Flying Crosses for heroism, 25 Air Medals--one with a "V" for valor--and two Vietnam Crosses of Gallantry for valor, plus other medals.[4]

The one mission with Del I remember most was when we were called to evacuate eleven Vietnamese babies and small children who'd been playing together in a village when the Viet Cong dropped a mortar round on top of them. We swooped in to salvage what remained. Villagers quickly laid their maimed and bloody bodies on our hard metal deck like a collection of broken Asian dolls.

Del did what he could for those still alive. As I was flying back to our aid station at LZ Hawk Hill, I glanced over my shoulder. He was sitting cross-legged in the center of our cargo compartment. Our cargo doors were open and the refreshing slipstream ruffled the scant clothing of these wounded children. Del was cradling and rocking the smallest of these babies in his arms. There was a single "frag" wound in her forehead. She was quite dead. This baby had been killed by the enemy as casually as a spider is crushed under a jungle boot. Lying naked, except for a tiny white top, her body fluids had drained and drenched the flimsy towel in which he held her.

Tears were rolling down Del's cheeks as he continued rocking her. At one point, his intercom button was accidentally depressed. We all heard, as he repeated over and over and over again to himself, "You poor little kid, you poor little kid..." It's at traumatic moments like that when we discovered how really heavy dead babies can be.

In Dust Off flying, there was nothing special we could do in the face of ominous death statistics except attempt to save others from this terrible fate. As the son of a Protestant minister, I was raised to believe that God decides when a person's final second comes. When it does arrive, there isn't much anyone can do about it. It just happens on its own. But all of us did the best we could at standing between our patients and a final rendezvous with Graves Registration.

These young dead soldiers, children and civilian men and women are now shadows that will continue to fall across my soul as long as God allows me to live. I witnessed hundreds and hundreds of them slip away like water through fingers day and night. Everyone dies. Sometime. Eventually. You can't get out of it. Death always wins. Most of these people didn't intend to die. It wasn't on their day planners or anything, it simply transpired on its own. Many of those casualties probably thought they had lots of time left. But their hourglasses suddenly ran out of sand. In their specific cases, they were dead wrong.

It's true. Vietnam *was* a 24-hour-a-day, real-life, drive-by shooting gallery...a very easy place to die. War is gruesome. It's violent. It's undignified. It wasn't the way any rational person would envision meeting their Maker.

In every war, some people return intact and others don't. My soul sorrow and ultimate survivor's guilt at having witnessed so many dead and wounded is not easily dismissed. As decades drift by, the pain becomes less intense...but it never disappears. It's as though I don't want it to disappear because I never want to forget what I saw and experienced or those I met who were so vulnerable and courageous in battle.

As a pilot in the Dust Off business, I knew there were heavy odds that I might die doing my job. But what was more important to me was the kind of person I was in the face of that fact. Regardless of how our patients were wounded, or how bad, they were my responsibility. They were someone's son or daughter, brother, sister, cousin or close friend. That's why I wasn't afraid to take risks in an effort to give them an opportunity to be reunited with their loved ones again, because I knew my fellow flight crews and comrades would do the same for me.

In that year in Southeast Asia, I witnessed accidents, the wounding and deaths of soldiers, civilians and children in nearly every way imaginable. And there were also those other patients we carried suffering from snake bites, plague, leprosy, gas gangrene, cholera, malaria and a variety of other tropical diseases. As has been the case with soldiers in previous wars, such chaotic scenes, tragedies and confrontational experiences are something I can't expunge from my memory bank...even nearly 50 years later.

I've discovered that combat is an extraordinary setting for issues of the heart. The stakes are immense while attempting to survive moment by moment in a brutal and unforgiving landscape of perpetual terror, blood and devastation. Everyone involved is under a massive level of stress. It's human drama at its zenith. What remains with me to this day, and every day, is the randomness of death that encompassed that incomprehensible world. When I faced termination from life, and was forced to view those intimidating spectacles--front row and center--it had a tendency to focus and command my attention. Those heartrending scenes will haunt me as long as I have breath.

The sights, sounds and smells of war may never disappear. Yet I've been granted a special loan called "time" which I must make effective use of for the sake of my patients and comrades who cannot share this same benefit. My duty now is to do the best I can in remembering and informing others of what these soldiers, who no longer have a voice, accomplished and endured. It's the greatest honor I can provide to them.

Life after combat has been like climbing to the top of a monster roller coaster. This has resulted in a lot of ups and downs. Sometimes I've even been turned upside down. Yet there is nowhere to go but forward. So I've learned to hang on tight and attempt to enjoy the ride for as long as it lasts.

###

Notes

[1] John Bartlett, <u>Familiar Quotations</u> 14th Edition (Boston, 1968), 620a.

[2] David A. Maurer, "Vietnam Vet Reunited with Helicopter Pilot Who Helped Save His Life," *Charlottsville (Virginia) The Daily Journal*, 13 August 2015, 4.

[3] Peter Dorland and James Nanney, *Dust Off: Aeromedical Evacuation in Vietnam* United States Army Center of Military History, Washington, DC, 1982), *117*.

[4] SP4 Robert A. Spangler, "Dustoff Medic's Story," *European Stars and Stripes*, 23 December 1970, 3.

Lt. Col. Robert B. Robeson, USA (Ret)

Robert Robeson retired, as a lieutenant colonel, after a 27-year military career living and flying on three continents and later served as a newspaper managing editor and columnist. He has a BA in English from the University of Maryland—College Park and has completed extensive undergraduate and graduate work in journalism at the University of Nebraska—Lincoln. He's a life member of the National Writers Association, VFW, Dustoff Association and Distinguished Flying Cross Society. A four-time, international Amy Writing Award winner, he has also been awarded fifteen George Washington Honor Medals for essays, articles and speeches on freedom by the National Award Juries of the Freedoms Foundation at Valley Forge, Pennsylvania. He's been decorated eight times for valor, earned 26 Air Medals, plus a Bronze Star, and received numerous other medals and awards from two governments. He lives in Lincoln, Nebraska with his wife, Phyllis, of 50 years. And he still dislikes sudden loud noises.

Photo - (L-R) Col. D.W. Pratt (now deceased)—95th Evacuation Hospital commander—presents Capt. Robert Robeson with his second Distinguished Flying Cross and second Air Medal with "V" at the 236th Medical Detachment headquarters at Red Beach in Da Nang, South Vietnam in late 1969. (Photo courtesy of Robert Robeson)

Tin Cup, Colorado 1982
BY *MATTHEW TREDWAY*

I caught an occasional glimpse of the range cowboys checking in at the ranch. These guys tended to cows from multiple ranches grazing each summer on forest permits. This allowed a summer's hay crop to be grown and harvested in home pastures for winter's feed. I was starstruck by these cowboys, adorned in boots, spurs, hats and leather chaps. They stayed in high mountain cow camps and rode their horses daily, keeping track of the herd. They seemed quick with a laugh, skilled with the animals, meticulous in dress, and carefree. They didn't seem to need supervision, creating and maintaining their own schedules. They were pros. As much as I wanted to do that, it would be years before I was qualified to do that work—but I was hired well before then.

I spent my early summers working on Gunnison area ranches during hay season. The son of a college professor and a teacher, my parents were intellectuals, but happy to let me live out my childhood in small town style. The fact that some of the ranchers provided room and board was a bonus, and took pressure off of our house filled with 3 other brothers. By eighth-grade summer, I was driving a scatter-rake behind haying crews, gathering the remaining hay after the main harvest. It was heaven for a fourteen-year-old—driving through beautiful mountain valley pastures, and getting paid to boot.

My first job on a ranch lasted two weeks. Afterward I was hooked. I craved the life. The smell of being outside, the fresh cut hay, and feeling responsible. I was the youngest, least-experienced on the crew, so I inevitably got the jobs no one else wanted. That didn't faze me. Soon, I was transferred to other jobs, like hand-lifting the bales onto truck beds from the field, then unloading and stacking them in the barn. Sundrenched, and empowered, we were our own bosses, and thrived on the physical challenges.

My first foray as a range rider was in Tincup, a ghost town in central Colorado. I was a horse wrangler for a former coach who operated a horseback riding operation for tourists. At 10,200 feet, the town was isolated; eight miles of semi maintained dirt road to the nearest phone. Tincup was three blocks square, with about thirty dwellings. A small summer population, with zero year-round residents, the town hall, to this day, hosts a Friday night square dance in the summers that attract people from miles around. Tincup had a colorful past as a gold mining mecca, including stories of several sheriff's being killed by the wild miners over the years. Now, the seasonal residents hailed from every corner of the United States, and

172

shared the desire for a quiet mountain life. Surrounded by forests, the cool mountain air was laced with the smell of pine trees, and wood-burning stoves in the morning.

Ringed by the Continental Divide, its thousands of acres was used every third year to graze three hundred cows and calves for the summer. It was the cowboy's job to move these cows around to various parts of the range, drop salt blocks, watch for sickness, and doctor the cows in need. The daily routine included saddling horses and riding a different loop through the vast range. Every couple of weeks, we would move the entire herd to another part of the range, to prevent overgrazing. Usually this would consume at least half a day. The process would be loud and hectic, as mothers would call loudly to their calves, trying in vain to keep them close. Upon reaching our destination, we would hold them in place till all were reunited. After the confusion of the move, if they were not paired, they would instinctively walk back and meet at the last place they nursed. That would undo all the work we had just put in. When the chorus of cows settled down, we knew all was right.

It's indescribable being on a horse on a cool, quiet mountain morning, with fog lifting off the beaver ponds, quietly riding among grazing cows—the smells of saddle leather, horse sweat, pine trees and crushed grass and soil being churned up under hooves.

We were on constant watch for larkspur, a plant that if eaten, can kill a cow. There were stories of cows dying quickly after eating the plant. We took care to keep that from happening. It's ironic that another big ailment for cows on the high range was pulmonary edema, the same problem climbers sometimes have at altitude.

Another chore was just good PR: keeping the cows out of town. Summer residents, while tougher than most, didn't appreciate them mowing their grass and leaving manure to step in. The whole area was an open range and it was the responsibility of the landowner to fence animals out. We did our best to move them elsewhere.

We would never have gotten the job were it not for an incident that occurred between the previous rider and disgruntled people living in town. Justin Hall, the range's former rider, was a legend fit for the big screen. He was over six feet tall, wore a black hat and tall black boots with big silver spurs, and had a black eye patch and a huge, booming voice. To make this picture perfect, he rode a tall, sure-footed mule rather than a horse. Stories abound about his great wit. A rancher once inquired as to the number of cattle in a particular area on the range. Justin responded, "around twenty head I think". Scoffing, the rancher replied, "Justin, can you even count to twenty"? "Only if l take off my boots" he replied quickly, "Six toes on one foot, four on the other"

According to legend, Justin had been around town asking people politely to get rid of the larkspur around their houses. A fashionable-looking flower, many people dug them from the surrounding meadows to plant in their gardens. The townsfolk obliged his request. All except the local preacher, Jim Hittle.

Hittle not only refused to remove the plant from his gardens, he planted more. This didn't sit well with Justin Hall, who took it as a personal attack. Running low on patience, Justin rode up on his big mule one afternoon to the Hittle household, located at the only real intersection in town, across from the church. When he finally found Mr. Hittle, he rode close, and looking down his nose from the saddle, used his booming voice to question Hittles choice of garden flowers. What began as a civil conversation quickly escalated into a screaming match. Hittle eventually retreated to the house, locked the door and drew the shades. A small crowd gathered. The retreat riled Justin to the point that he rode his mule as close to the house as he could. To be sure the message passed through the walls of the cabin, he delivered this speech in his fullest, baritone volume, and capped it off with this proclamation: "Hittle, I don't know God, never met him … but if he has sons of bitches like you running his outfit, I don't believe I care to."

There was enough backlash over Justin's outburst that the Forest Service reconsidered hiring him the next season. The Forest Service was effectively leasing public land to these ranchers. We were in the right place at the right time and were hired to be the riders for the Tincup pool in 1978. I spent many subsequent summers in Tincup and the surrounding area looking after these cows.

We lived in a one room log cabin with a corral and a shed out back. Our horses for the next day were kept in the pen and fed hay, with the remainder of our remuda held in a horse pasture a couple miles from town. We usually had three or four each, so we could ride a horse, then give it a few days to recover before going out again. In addition to riding, I had a supply of leather, and a stitcher, in the evenings I made saddles and chaps for myself and most of the other cowboys

Every morning we caught our horses early, then headed to a different part of the range. We found the cows in the area and looked at each one carefully, monitoring their feed and health. You can see a lot about a cow's health by glancing at its head and tail, watching it walk, and observing how it reacts to people. We roped and doctored sick cows for the common ailments we could diagnose. In our herd of several hundred, we usually caught one or two a day. It was an exhilarating part of the job, particularly when the patient was a twelve hundred-pound bull.

Newly married, my wife, Dana, and I lived in that small cabin with a wood- burning stove for cooking and heat, no running water and an outhouse a hundred and fifty feet away.

176

She worked in the local restaurant for tips, and spent afternoons studying for the CPA exam and hiking. I made $600 a month, but we felt flush; it was more money than we ever had before. We spent a magical summer at 10,200 feet.

Another job was to keep cattle out of a basin located above the old Gold Cup mine, an active mine in the late 1800s. Now it was just skeletons of buildings and piles of tailings, high in a valley lush with aspen trees, grass and water. The abundant grass made it a valuable part of the range. With the aid of a fence, steep hillsides and constant vigilance, we actively worked to avoid accidental poisoning from the scattered patches of larkspur. We made it a point to check this part of the range every couple of days.

One late August day, riding up the valley to check those cows, I noticed that the Gold Cup gate was open. Heart sinking, I galloped to the fence opening and saw telltale cow tracks through the mud leading up the hill. I smelled the death before ever seeing a body. I rounded the corner of a trail and saw several cows grazing, and a couple of bodies down. My horse shied at the rank odor. One, two, then a third. I got around the living cows and started them back down the draw. It would become one of the most horrible days of my life. Four, five, six, dead animals, it was rapidly becoming a nightmare. The cows represented the only income the ranches had for the coming year. Each was worth more money than I made in a month.

Seven. Holy shit, just how bad is this going to get? I spent the afternoon cutting the ear tags off the dead cows and stowing them in my saddlebags. I rode my horse back and forth for a couple of hours, in ever-growing circles to ensure I didn't miss any, alive or dead. The calves of the dead milled around adding to the nauseating scene. It was late enough in the summer and the calves had grown enough that they would survive, but would I?

The ride home was the worst I can remember. How could I possibly explain? This was not a mistake like shipping something to a wrong address, or breaking a machine. Animals that I had fussed and worried over all summer, had died. And I really cared. That gate was a huge part of my job and I had failed. I unsaddled my horse, and turned him into the pasture. I tossed my saddle and headstall in the back of my truck and began to drive slowly. I stopped by the cabin and explained the disaster to Dana. We were paralyzed with fear. Leaving her in Tincup, I planned my explanation as I rolled down the long eight miles of dirt road to use the phone.

There was no one else to blame. Granted, the gate had been left open by someone else, but I should have been there to monitor it before all those cows got in there. I had just checked it a couple of days ago. I arrived at the Taylor Park trading post around dusk and drove up to the payphone at the store. Tourists and fishermen lingered on the wooden deck out front. I smelled smoke from the grill in the cafe, chugging out the cheeseburgers for the hungry adventurers. Rummaging, l collected some change from the ashtray of my truck and walked over to the payphone. Hiding behind a hat pulled low and range scarf up over my mouth, I was sure everyone knew of my mistake. Dreading every step, I tried to walk quietly, but my spurs jingled as I sauntered across the parking lot. The phone swallowed the quarters and I dialed the ranch headquarters. I wanted privacy, but even as l dialed, someone else was already lined up behind me to use the only payphone for miles. To make matters worse, I was dialing a party line number. The call could be listened to by all the ranches on the Tomichi creek line. There was no hiding what happened.

Fighting off tears as the phone rang, my stomach wrenched, my hands started sweating and my heart tightened. I heard, "hello". I described the tragedy to my boss, Paul Taramarcaz, fumbling a long emotional explanation. Expecting his wrath, I almost felt worse when his kind voice talked me down and explained that it happens, a response I never expected. It made a world of difference. That compassion is how I want to react every time I'm on the other side of the story.

During the days following, I was filled with feelings of unreality, like this couldn't have happened. Our carefree existence was turned upside down. Guilt created a combination of irritation, and hopelessness. Those feelings fueled multiple trips per day to check the gate in addition to my regular duties. As the world righted itself in the coming weeks, my vigilance was at a highpoint. I vowed to do everything in my power to prevent a repeat.

The summer ended well. No more epic issues. The cows were gathered and herded home in early fall. I learned that I coped better than I ever expected to. I learned that I had so much to be grateful for, like a good job, an unbelievably supportive wife, and caring boss. I learned to appreciate every day. Those lessons have stuck with me, and I attribute them to the person I am today. Though painful at the time, I count this as one of my significant life experiences. While life ultimately took me down other paths, those summers created countless memories which I have relieved often during a 30-year teaching career.

Matthew Tredway

Matt Tredway and his wife Dana, call Steamboat, Colorado home. Matt has been very involved in the community for 32 years. He instructed Math and Science in the public schools as well as coached. They have two daughters that now reside in Nashville

Matt grew up in Gunnison, Co., and spent summers as a cowboy for local ranches. Always the outdoor enthusiast he founded and was the director of Everything Outdoor Steamboat. EOS is designed to give students a chance to experience outdoor activities including rock and ice climbing, backpacking, winter mountaineering, kayaking, and horse packing. He states," There is no greater thrill than to witness a student succeed in a challenge that they were convinced would defeat them".

Matt now heads a construction company and is a partner in a real estate development company. He continues to serve on several boards, including the Steamboat Springs Winter Sports Club.

The Ring

By Trudy Wells-Meyer

"The road to heaven and the human heart is amazingly short when priceless diamonds from the past are involved." — *Anonymous*

As I arrived at the downtown Scottsdale mortuary, the home of final goodbyes and viewings, where countless sad hearts had gone before, I opened the door with a heavy hand. The body of my Arizona Mom, Margo Becket, was ready for me to add the final touch; my first time to style hair on a deceased person.

I still can feel my slow, hesitant steps toward the casket near the back wall, feeling safe from a distance. Unknown emotions surrounded me for what I might encounter. I stood in front of Margo's rich, opulent casket, experiencing the opposite of what I had visualized; I found out that "perfect" does not always look like we imagine.

I gasped in disbelief as I stared at Margo's peaceful face, with the rare smile I had loved for years. All gussied up to be seen in heaven, she showed pain no longer. The word beautiful was simply too weak. However, one thing remained, to fix that flat hair and perform my magic with her favorite hair style — an act of love.

I felt a sense of gratitude being here with my dead client whom I had known for more than thirty years. This was my parting gift, a promise for Margo to look regal one last time for eternity. A lump arose in the back of my throat as I gazed at her favorite ivory and gold dress, which I helped pick out for a fancy black-tie wedding sixteen years ago. Her cherished pearls and earrings were glowing in the light and her smile expressed, "I look good".

On her folded hands, her most treasured diamond ring, a spectacular anniversary gift from Stewart, was missing. I was in shock, I had never seen her without it. Thoughts of her promise swirled in my brain; words exchanged on countless Fridays at the beauty shop:

"You fix my hair when I die — the ring is yours."

With unsure hesitation I touched her lifeless hair. Curls were needed for sure. As I tried to achieve the style countless women admired constantly, I got nervous. My hands shook when I detected her head slightly raised on a piece of wood, on a wood-pillow, glued on the back of the skull and stapled. I had chills. Where did Margo's hair go? Her forehead was never that big; it had been pulled up high for the skin to look tight.

Her beauty wrecked but still evident, I realized only the front and top mattered for styling. My usual routine of whipping hair into instant glamour would not happen. Give her bangs! A new look to parade in heaven, yet I felt guilty, Margo had never desired a different style.

***

With a mad nobility and regal elegance, demanding and stern, Margo Maria Becket knew what she wanted. She possessed an odd, recognizable voice, a voice that was loud — shrieky almost. Margo was my weekly client for years, my Arizona Mom, a widow with an extreme sense of style that was somehow more noticeable in a desert town, where fanatical casualness lets people dress down and blame the heat. In Arizona, a flip-flop state, I mean shoes, they show up half-naked at the supermarket, at restaurants — anywhere, anytime. Margo's fierce intention to look one's best every day matched my own.

Her shy smile had a hard time surfacing, yet when it did, still today, I can see it shine. Mrs. Becket entered the new, fancy Mahogany hair salon, one Friday afternoon to basically check me out and interview me.

That same morning, Margo had her hair done up north at a slow-paced, less busy Scottsdale salon. My ex-assistant Maxine, the kindest person I know, shampooed her hair. Sadly, with heavy heart, I had let Maxine go because she was sick with daily pains and couldn't keep up with my schedule at Mahogany's, nor handle the pressure of pleasing as many clients as I demanded of her each day. As she listened to Margo Becket's weekly complaining, mostly about her dislike of the various stylists who tried but couldn't fix her hair, Maxine whispered in her soap-filled ears,

"Go and see Trudy downtown, at Mahogany's."

Margo yelled, "Who?"

Mrs. Becket searched for a salon named Mahogany on Indian School Road. That same afternoon she entered and commanded attention not only by her appearance but by a voice that could scare a fish. "Where is Trudy?" Her voice echoed to the back corner of our buzzing salon, where my hair-heaven was located.

On that frantic Friday, Ricardo, my boss and salon owner, had walked Mrs. Becket to my bustling corner to introduce us. This lady, who knew the language of couture, caused me to look up, stop cutting hair, and nearly forget the client in my chair. Margo's bashful almost-smile surprised me; however, I stared in astonishment at the gorgeous jewelry layered around her neck and ears and at the way she held her hands, showing off four rings. A dazzling, huge diamond ring on her index finger triggered my heart to hiccup.

My busy schedule left me with anxious speculations: Another new weekly customer? I watched her look around and put her hand with the eye-catching ring on her mouth, as if to say, No way. She gasped at my waiting clients. I knew waiting would scare her off.

Wrong. Margo Becket's newfound hairstylist passed the interview, answering questions that sounded desperate. She hollered chants about hair never short enough — too long in the wrong places — color never blonde enough.

"Trudy, can you fit me in, once a week, and work with me?" shouted the classy lady with hopeful eyes.

"I can try. I cut hair to look good, not to be short," I answered, flashing a smile. I wished I could whip her hair into place right then, since I knew instantly which style would look good on this hairdresser-hating, unhappy person.

On the way out, this stunning woman with bad hair made a standing appointment for every Friday — a simply unheard-of decision without experiencing and knowing how I would style her hair.

***

Margo Becket turned out to be a dream client. No complaints about her hair or waiting her turn. She adored one style, my unique, signature look that added youth to her face; hair flipping away above her left eye, a backcombed but not helmet-like hairdo with a twist of blonde glamour.

They called her "sexy grandma".

Our upscale salon became Mrs. Becket's weekly home. For twenty-eight years her outing to the beauty shop, at 12:30 every

Friday, included listening to her valued Swiss-born hair-stylist, Trudy, gibbering about her extremely happy marriage. It reminded Margo, widowed for many years, of her own past life. Her unique smile would appear, and with faraway eyes she would ask about Lew, Trudy's brilliant, with a degree from the school of life, genius-husband.

Margo loved to compare Lew with Stewart, her long-time husband who had passed away of complications from a heart-attack, too long ago. Her smile grew titanic as she transported herself back to her happy life, listening to how Trudy could not imagine a day without Lew touching her face.

Over and over Margo would ask about the gentle man who had become my world. Lew, like Stewart, was one of those men whose presence attracted notice in any gathering, anywhere. Lew radiated a positive, constant smile, a distinctive tilting of his head as he fitted his cigarette between two fingers, not ordinarily used. "Just like my Stewart," Margo would sigh with dreamy eyes. She relived her life weekly at the beauty shop.

Mrs. Becket was in awe of my blissful, whirl-wind life and remarkably successful career; however, her questions most Fridays were the same, about my love life. She endlessly compared my stories with hers about her beloved Stewart — a happy life, no doubt. Memories, like random photographs, filled her mind as she touched and caressed the amazing, huge diamond ring on her right index finger, a spectacular dome setting studded with enormous, glittering jewels.

I stared at the blinding beauty once a week. Everybody did. The ring was a seventeenth anniversary gift with seventeen gigantic diamonds. At various times I listened to that romantic instant when Margo's Stewart presented his wife with the magical surprise. Proudly she wore the precious ring every day, even on her daily walk to feed the ducks at a pond close to home. Some Fridays she handed me that magnificent rock to wear while I combed her hair. The first time, I hardly believed how perfectly it fit on my index finger.

I joked, "Margo, now watch your hair turn out even more glamorous." I felt the stares of my waiting customers. During my days at any salon in different parts of America I was known for my love of jewelry. Six rings on my hands a norm and always matching my outfits.

"How can she work with all those rings?" Customers whispered and mumbled.

When Mrs. Becket entered, always on time like clockwork, she paraded her elegant way with hair still in place after one week of not washing it. (Those were the days.) Curious clients stared and admired her at our hectic, high-class salon.

Ardis, another long-time weekly client, a divorcée who had just "landed" a new millionaire husband she met on a plane to Denver, sat in my chair on one such Friday. Her rare sense of humor provided weekly entertainment for most clients. Ardis, ready to leave and be seen with her high-styled hair watched Margo join the Friday-gang.

Ardis yelled, "What the f*** are you doing here? Your hair looks great!"

"Well, I sleep alone," Margo shouted. The whole salon giggled.

Nothing could stop or spoil Margo's Friday at the beauty shop. Her escape to the hair salon turned into fun and enjoyment, and ultimately, she felt glamorous again when she left. Margo sat patiently on one of the side chairs along the wall, always the end one so as not to seem pushy while waiting her turn. Often, with a ghost of a wink directed at me, she'd say in unusually soft-spoken words, "When I come here, I don't plan anything else." With a thank-you on my silent lips I gave her a heartfelt nod with love for her eyes only.

My Arizona Mom, who helped me bear my hectic schedule, whose words remain unforgettable: "Your talent is a gift from God; what you make of it is your gift to God."

If judged by the hair-world on how many clients waited at one time — I had to be the winner. Margo taught me that pressure is a privilege, to enjoy my gift of making women happy. I lived to find the perfect hairstyle for each one.

Now retired, I reminisce about the days during my artistic American hair life, times when I was jolted with the force of my own creativity. Somehow I knew what to do straightaway and how to handle hair with ease, the ever-glowing crown of women, my fussy male clientele included.

The dynamics of my world reflected each day on my happy face. Hair is power. Not to say I didn't know rejection. The more hopefully I anticipated the start of a client-stylist relationship, the more painful it was at the end, with no call-back and cancellations for reasons seldom known or understood.

***

After twenty-two years, Mahogany's closed its doors. The building, in the way of a main street to be widened, resulted in money to be made for the happy owner. My clients and I moved to a gorgeous new salon, an ex-jewelry store with soft lighting. Customers' skin and hair appeared to look even better.

A promise started one memorable Friday. Roy Becket, Margo's younger son from Chicago, had come to visit. In mother's fancy car, he drove her to the front entrance, for the usual weekly appointment. I was flipping my Arizona Mom's hair into shape and style when Roy walked in to pick her up for a late lunch.

In her shrill voice she yelled, "Roy, come here!" She pointed to the exquisite ring on her aged hand. "When I am dead and leave this world, I want you to give this ring to Trudy. She promised to always wear it at the beauty shop when she creates magic with her clients' hair."

Her words echoed around the glamourous salon on this unusually calm Friday. Clients gasped.

***

Retirement didn't stop me from doing Margo's hair. I went to her home. No longer every Friday, we met on whatever day that worked, when Lew and I were in Scottsdale. Our continuous travelling required unique planning at times. My trips to the assisted-living rehab center, where Margo resided for weeks because of a critical fall, turned into memorable fun at their tiny in-house salon. I paraded her like a queen in a wheelchair down the long corridor so she could show off her hair to many of the elderly residents. Some of the ladies' hopeful eyes and whispers, can you do my hair? still haunt me.

Roy, the big-town Chicago son, took care of his mother after falls happened too often, caused by age and too much medication. The first fall in her bathroom broke her jaw; later, in her small kitchen, she lay for hours with nobody to find her, nobody to call 9-1-1. A broken hip led to other extreme problems. More medication? Why so much? How do pills know where to go once swallowed —, to the left, to the right, where? A pill-cocktail in your stomach? Margo remained bound to a wheelchair, leaving her angry and hopeless. Roy moved in with Mom.

***

My final trip to fix her hair at her home, in the fancy dining room, will linger in my heart always. On this specific day in 2008 — ironically, a Friday — Margo's frail state seemed calmer; pain gone maybe? Her yelling and screaming had stopped. The imperious voice was mercifully silenced. I sensed an aura it's time. She held my hand with a touch of love so strong for a weak, skinny lady, a parting gift I would cherish for a long time. Even now I can feel the need to hug Margo longer than usual, not letting go.

At the bend outside the entry door I turned. I smiled without much joy, but still a smile. Roy had moved her wheelchair under the open door. I waved, blowing a kiss at my Arizona Mom with perfect hair to return to bed and sleep — an instant flattened mess in the back, no doubt. As I walked down the balcony corridor to the elevator of the Beckets' condo complex, I experienced a chill, as if knowing it was the last time. Everything suddenly was still. Not even the birds were singing.

***

A shrill cell phone ringing interrupted the new-found pride in my retired, like a vacation life, cutting roses in our incredibly awesome garden. I listened to Margo's devoted son Roy, his sad voice with the news of Mom's death. I leaned back against the wrought iron rail, the brilliant glittering lake behind me, Camelback Mountain in the distance, while my soil-covered

192

hand held the phone. I rubbed my eyes, Roy's deliberate words echoed in my ears, "Mom has gone to heaven."

In that instant my eyes stopped on a single yellow rose — the only yellow in the middle of all the countless, various pink ones. Yellow — Margo's favorite color. I trembled. I must have looked downright ill. Shivering at this heart-stopping moment, as one spectacular yellow rose let me see Margo as big as life. Like the opening of a floodgate, I wept. Timing in life — the mystery of it . . . oh, I wondered why time after time I had purchased and planted a yellow rose bush amidst varieties of pink, my favorites. Now I knew.

"When is the funeral?" I stammered.

I could feel Roy's tears and hear them as he whispered in a voice that didn't sound like his. I hardly had the heart to tell Roy of our upcoming month-long trip, arranged and planned long ago, leaving the morning of the funeral.

I felt his sorrow and personal sense of tragedy as I told him about staring at this single yellow rose in full bloom in our garden, knowing full well Roy knew what yellow roses meant to his mom. I cried uncontrollably, knowing that grief has many faces.

Nevertheless, I knew immediately what to do, and the full realization struck with such force that I threw the chair over with the shock of it. I must go to fix Margo's hair. I rushed into the house to look up the mortuary's phone number. A promise I never thought I could keep had come alive — a promise — Margo's often spoken words on numerous Fridays during her standing appointment for 28 years, her wish for her hair to look perfect when she arrives in heaven. *"You know you have to fix my hair when I die."*

After an exceptionally successful career, where customers lined up, one may wonder why I had never, in all those years, performed any doing-the-hair service at a mortuary. I simply believed I couldn't.

"Let's hope God calls you on Friday afternoon, after you had your hair done." My hesitant, unconvinced answer left Margo frowning each time.

She passed away on a Friday, early in the morning.

I took a deep breath. On the edge of decision, I winced as if in pain. I couldn't clear my mind of Margo's words. Wishing them gone did not convince me they had never been spoken. I dialed the number of the mortuary. An enormously kind voice set me at ease. We arranged a time on Monday, the day before the funeral, the day before our long trip.

***

I silently prayed as I labored on her final good-bye-hairstyle with three-day-old dead hair in my hands, foreign to my touch. Hair I had known for more than thirty years, now let me down — I felt like a failure — my final hairdo for Margo ended up a new look for eternity. I hoped her days in heaven turned into fun, parading her new hair style, good enough to last forever.

Roy, who had promised to meet me at the mortuary, his eyes watching me from the back of the room, had added to my nervousness. He had come up behind me, "Mom looks beautiful."

He joined my tears. His words helped tremendously.

"The ring is missing. Margo, without her ring?" I mumbled.

Roy answered with a voice just above a whisper, "It's yours now." He choked up. "Mom wanted you to have her favorite ring. A promise is a promise."

Startling feelings emerged as my thoughts traveled to that Friday when the promise had started, for me to have the admired ring, if I agreed to fix Margo's hair one final time, at the mortuary, for her to travel in style to the big garden in the sky.

The desire to give that dynamic gem to her hairstylist, not written in Margo's will, became an issue with the Beckets' huge estate. Roy, as the executor, had to convince the lawyers. His brother, who never visited his mom, the estranged son, had to be contacted. He couldn't have cared less.

***

After our extended travel, I found a most heartfelt thank-you note from Roy between bills and junk-mail, that had been held by the post office. He wrote to please let him know instantly when we returned to town, to get together, so that he could hand me his mother's promise, the ring.

We met at a small bistro, Margo had liked, near the Beckets' home, now Roy's winter home. We drove up at the same time. I waved fiercely as he stepped out of the Lexus car, a skinny, tiny cigar in his mouth. Was he nervous? I didn't know he still smoked.

I rushed to his parked car. He opened the trunk and bent down to reach for a golden box with shaking hands. When he looked up and saw me, he stared with a face of crushing sadness. He pointed to my outfit: my dressy sweater in shimmering gold with a matching silk flower, identical in color to the golden box and the ring.

"Mom's color," he stated. Margo's favorite, the elegant gold color which she had worn on plenty of Fridays. I had dressed in her honor. Roy sobbed.

Always, forever I will feel that exquisite moment of lift-off — in my hands a golden box glistening in the sunlight. A swirl of excited anticipation gained altitude, soaring higher and higher. A promise had become real. With eyes transfixed at the brilliance of the diamonds in the Arizona sunshine, in a busy parking lot, my hands trembled. Yet the moment when I put the ring on my finger, the spell broke. I knew full well it was a perfect fit.

My knees buckled. Unsurpassed nostalgia and tears turned into sobs. Fridays of the past flashed in front of my eyes:

Margo's joy-filled face had watched me put that jewel on my finger — now, the ring was mine. A sense of closeness to a lady, who claimed to be my Arizona Mom, up in that spot of grace for the rest of time, filled my heart. Closeness expressed in a ring of unprecedented magnificence — a ring, the sign of eternity. How exceptional, when a client and hairstylist share a bond lasting a lifetime.

The value of all those diamonds is not measured by their size but by the love given to a girl from far across the sea . . . Some ties are simply meant to be. Grief turned into intimacy as if a treasure had been transported to the pocket of my heart. The road to heaven is paved with memories. I could see Margo smile.

Don't cry because it's over; smile because it happened.

During our lunch together, when that tower of diamonds had become mine, Roy asked, "When will you work the next time?"

"Tomorrow!" I shouted too loud. It had been six weeks since my last working days. My exciting retirement still included several longtime clients at the same salon; some for more than forty years.

Roy answered with haste, "You know mother wants you to wear the ring each time you work." He clearly knew of Mom's wish for me to show the jewel to the ladies at the salon.

The gate between thoughts and words opened and let out feelings of awe over the miracle of perfect timing. Our joyful tears for Mom merged with sadness and happy memories.

That exquisite gift, an act of love, I wear with a proud heart. Always will.

"Death leaves a heartache no one can heal. Love leaves a memory no one can steal."
— Richard Puz

Trudy Wells-Meyer

Trudy Wells – Meyer, Swiss born, is a retired successful hair designer. She writes Poetry and short stories in her second language. She arrived in New York, from the German-speaking part of Switzerland, on June 18, 1965. She traveled on a massive ocean liner from England, her home for the longest days of her young life, surrounded by water, on her own, all by herself. Each moment of the voyage took her farther away from the only home she knew, growing up poor in a modest Swiss village, in an old house, where even dreaming had its limits, never knowing of Switzerland's admired beauty worldwide. For hours, she gazed at the brilliant glittering sea, like dancing diamonds; endless time to wonder and doubt that dream of Coming to America — fear a constant companion. She was 23.

Trudy hopes her writing remains necessary in a life filled with feelings and emotions where her passionate mind believes in the power of words.

Woven

By Patricia Walkow

I directed the feather duster across the surface of the
Navajo rug, removed the beautiful weaving from its hook-and-
loop strip attached to a length of light-weight wood holding it on
the wall, flipped it, and dusted the equally attractive reverse
side. "Tapestry quality" was the phrase the salesperson used to
describe it at the high-end American Indian arts shop in touristy
Scottsdale, Arizona. "So expertly woven there is no front, no
back. Worth every penny."

I've had this remarkable weaving for many years. Woven
of wool shorn from sheep the weaver raised, it is tinted with
soft-toned, natural dyes from desert plants grown in the Wide
Ruins section of the Navajo Indian Reservation in eastern
Arizona. Within a single work of art, the rug is simultaneously an
example of pre-American cultural tradition and a slice of today's
Americana. I visited Wide Ruins and saw how the bands of pastel
colors in the sky met the warm tones of the earth at dusk. The
weaver captured that image in her mind and re-created it in a
rug. Purchased long before I moved out west, it made me want to
own more Navajo rugs.

After I dusted it, I moved on to my newest acquisition, a Crystal design, horizontally-banded and dyed in earth tones from native plants. It is almost the same tapestry quality of the Wide Ruins rug, but not quite. As I approached it in its spot above the fireplace, I remembered the night I purchased it at the monthly Navajo Rug Auction in Crownpoint, New Mexico, and smiled as the face of the ancient weaver came into view in my mind.

As I lifted the duster to brush the rug, I noticed white wool strands had emerged through the gray yarn at the lower left corner. I removed the weaving from its hanging strip and noticed the errant threads of wool seemed to form the letters "R" and "e" in cursive writing.

Squinting hard, I mumbled, *What the...?*

Damn, I am going to have to take it to the rug repair guru in town. I don't want it to unravel.

I held it at eye level, and the hairs on the back of my neck stood up. Dropping the rug on the floor, I ran out of the house, spooked.

Remembering.

* * *

At the auction in Crownpoint, a collector can bid on a Navajo rug, meet the weaver, and avoid paying the doubled or tripled price demanded by a retail shop. The weaver gets most of the money. Even better, the auction is barely a two-hour drive from my house near Albuquerque.

Travelling on I-40 West from Albuquerque, Crownpoint is northwest of Grants and northeast of Gallup. It is lonely, red-gold-rust-and-tan-toned country, peppered with hardy desert brush—the only green in sight—offset by a colorful sky of pink, salmon, russet, and blue. Mesas, sandy hills, distant mountains, and arroyos paint the landscape in scenes of desolate beauty, quiet and mysterious.

The auction I attended on a Friday night, two years ago, was crowded with weavers and collectors. The drive there was particularly beautiful on the early summer evening. As the sun melted below a western mesa, the terrain glowed, as it does only in the American Southwest.

What would I purchase?

I arrived early, as most experienced buyers do. I wanted ample time to examine the rugs for tightness of weave, symmetry, design, and quality. There were no restrictions. One can pick them up, turn them around, run fingers over the wool, and closely examine every inch woven by the artist. In the local school's hallway, each rug to be auctioned was numbered and tagged as the weaver registered it with the those who ran the event. Then, it was placed on a table inside the lunchroom. The weaver took a seat in the back of the large, airy cafeteria. All the buyers sat in front, armed with their bidding placards.

Three rugs caught my attention. One was a large Two Grey Hills design sporting its typical intricate pattern woven from black, white, and gray yarn—dramatic and popular. *Hmmm...the bidding will probably be high.* The second one was a banded Crystal rug, in soft tones of gray, beige, bronze, rust, and white and, I thought, woven by very experienced hands. It was subtle and understated. It probably won't go as high as the others, unless some shop owners are bidding. They'll recognize its quality. The third was a Yei rug of indigenous deities. *Probably will go higher than I want to spend for it.*

As the bidding progressed, I dropped out for the Two Grey Hills rug, and won the Yei weaving. The Crystal was one of the last items presented, and after some back-and-forth bidding repartee, I won it at about two hundred dollars more than I really wanted to pay for it.

But it is beautiful, I consoled myself.

After I paid for my purchase, I was gathering my things from my seat when I felt a gentle tug on my left sleeve. I turned to see a wizened, elderly, nut-brown oval face looking up at me. Being just a few inches over five feet myself, I marveled that she was so tiny. I towered over her, and it was an unusual experience for me.

This diminutive lady wore a full skirt of dark purple crushed velvet that almost swept the floor; her gray hair was tied in a knot at the nape of her neck, and the turquoise and silver squash blossom necklace she wore rested on her lavender blouse and seemed heavier than she probably weighed. The wrinkled old woman pointed a bony finger at my Crystal rug.

The young lady with her said, "My great grandmother made that rug you purchased." I held the rug's tag, and pointed to the name printed on it.

"You are Etta?" I asked the weaver.

She smiled a giant, nearly-toothless grin at me and nodded her head in agreement. Her small face lit up with sparkling light brown eyes.

"I am Fay." I ran my hands across the horizontal design. "This is a beautiful rug. I will hang it above the fireplace in my living room where I can enjoy it every day."

Etta's companion interpreted my words and Etta smiled broadly before quietly whispering something in her great granddaughter's ear.

"My great grandmother said this is the last rug she will ever weave. She has made many during her life, but her eyes are going dim, and her fingers stumble with the wool."

Glancing more closely at Etta's fingers, I saw they were gnarled, with exaggerated joints. I understood why the rug I had just purchased would be the last one she would ever make.

"I am glad you told me," I said to Lily, who by now had introduced herself. "The knowledge it is Etta's last rug makes it even more special to me."

Once again, Etta whispered something to her great granddaughter. I noticed Lily looked at her great grandmother with her head cocked and one eyebrow raised, as if suspicious of what Etta had just told her. Etta tugged at my sleeve again and pointed to Lily. I got the feeling Lily didn't want to translate what she had just heard, but Etta was insistent, pointing at Lily with her finger and then gesturing to me with her chin.

Lily cleared her throat.

"You don't have to believe this, but my great grandmother wants me to tell you this rug has magic in it. Magic that will take effect only after she passes to the next life."

"Magic?" I asked, somewhat amused. "What does that mean?" I asked Lily, but looked at Etta.

Once again Etta talked with Lily.

"It is good magic, if you live your life positively. Bad, if you don't."

"Well then, I guess I'd better be good," I responded with a lighthearted laugh that I hoped concealed my skepticism.

As we said our goodbyes, Etta grasped my arm, raised her hands to my face, and gently caressed my cheeks with her ancient palms. I grabbed her withered hands, lowered them, held on to them, and thanked her.

On the drive home, I glanced at both rugs folded neatly on the passenger front seat.

*Magic, huh...*I said to the Crystal rug as I glanced at it, barely able to see it in the dark.

I am not opposed to magic, I spoke aloud. *I can believe in serendipity and I am convinced that some coincidences are not really coincidences at all. Who knows what is out there, unseen and unknown?*

I patted the Crystal rug with my right hand. *We will have a good life together. You too, Yei.*

At home, I placed the Yei rug on my piano bench and found a spot above the fireplace for the new "magic" Crystal rug. The upper portion of my fireplace is curved, and the rug fit beautifully there. I could see it all the time from the living room or kitchen.

I tucked away Etta's statement about the rug being magical.

* * *

Despite the pleasant memory of the night I purchased the rug, I stayed outside until I calmed down enough to return to the fireplace, stunned to see more letters forming in the rug as it rested on the floor, where I had dropped it in fear. The phrase "Remember why" was clearly visible in woven script made of white yarn.

Summoning some courage and looking over my shoulder to be sure I was alone in the room, I picked the rug up and held it at arm's length. *Remember why?* I said aloud. *What does that mean? What was it Etta's great granddaughter said?*

"...my great grandmother wants me to tell you this rug has magic woven into it. Magic that will take effect only after she passes to the next life."

There was no rational explanation for the words on the gray band at the bottom of the rug. Was something mystical happening? Could Etta have been serious about the rug being enchanted? It unsettled me, but I was also extremely curious about what was happening. *What does "Remember why" mean? Did Etta die?* I placed the rug back on its holding strip above the fireplace.

That night, when I showed the words to Brian, my husband, he thought I was playing a trick on him, weaving the letters into the rug. I had no idea how to weave and decided to ignore the writing.

Yet, the appearance of the writing and the actual phrase that was woven haunted me for a few days. Nothing more happened until the morning I sat in my easy chair with my coffee and noticed the appearance of a new word: "you" was visible. "Remember why you" was interwoven in white across the lowest gray band.

*Why I **what**?* I demanded, my heart racing.

Another word took shape, as though woven by an invisible hand. The word "married" appeared. "Remember why you married" confronted me.

A cold shiver overcame me. I felt goose bumps rise all over my body. My voice trembled as I asked in a loud voice, Etta, is that you? Are you giving me a message? What are you trying to tell me? Is this really happening?

The word "him" emerged. A period materialized.

Remember why you married him.

My mouth flew open, dry as desert sand, and I covered it with both hands. I was trembling.

What is going on?

I rushed out of the house and sat on my patio, basking in the welcoming warmth of the summer air. My heart was pounding. *Was I losing my mind? Scotch...why didn't I bring scotch on ice out here? Brian won't believe me!*

After a half hour, I peeked inside and it seemed the rug had stopped creating a message. I stared at it for a while, one foot inside, and one still on the patio. Eventually, I went inside, but with a significant amount of trepidation.

For the rest of the day, I checked on the rug many times and kept my back to the wall, fearful some entity would surprise me from behind. The weaving had ceased, and no additional words were formed.

When Brian came home, I steered him to the rug. He gave me a quizzical look with his head tilted to the right as he read the message across the bottom band.

"What are you doing, Fay?"

"I'm not doing anything. The rug's doing it, or Etta is doing it."

"Etta? Who is Etta?"

I told Brian about Etta and what she told me the night I purchased the weaving: the rug had magical powers, but the magic would be evident only after she died.

"Well, don't think anything about it. It's nonsense," he said. With that, he retreated into his study, annoyed, I thought.

Or unsettled.

Does he think I spent the day weaving words into the rug...words that suggest I remember why I married him?

Then, inside my head...a lightning bolt.

We had been fighting a lot for a few months. There were no big issues, no major events in our lives that would have instigated constant discord. We were just getting on each other's nerves, picking at each other like warring siblings, and bickering about anything and everything. It was as though we had forgotten what attracted us to each other and kept us together. We'd been married over thirty years, and I thought it was probably normal now and then to be disgusted with each other, contemplate divorce for no good reason at all, and daydream about being single again. Didn't all couples go through stages like this in their marriage?

But the rug told me otherwise. *Was it instructing my heart to remember why I married Brian?* Whenever I did think about us, I wound up smiling about his antics and personality, his general good nature, his coming home every night, and his happiness to see me, despite that joy seeming tempered, lately.

I called to him. "Brian, would you mind coming into the living room for a minute?"

He emerged from his solitude, with a mug of tea in hand. "What is it?"

"You see the rug?" I asked him.

"Yes, I see it; what about it?"

"I remember why I married you. Do you want me to tell you?"

He offered a small smile as he glanced at the rug. "Sure."

I told him why I married him. I told him so many of the reasons were still valid, that I loved him, and I wanted to be with him in the future. We hugged.

When we released our embrace, Brian peered at the rug again, holding his chin between his right index finger and thumb. He was silent for what seemed like an eternal minute.

"Fay, what words do you see on the rug?"

"Remember why you married him."

He shook his head back and forth in disagreement.

"What's wrong?" I asked.

"It doesn't say 'Remember why you married him.'"

"Yes, it does...look at it."

"That's not what it says."

"Yes, it is...look at it!" I insisted.

"I am looking at it," he said. "It says 'Remember why you married her.'"

I disagreed, "No, it doesn't...it says 'him'."

We stood there, mute.

He turned to me and told me all the reasons why he married me, so many of them were still true, and he loved me and wanted to be with me in the future.

"This is creepy," Brian finally said. "Creepy, but I am grateful for the message."

"Me, too," I responded. "No one will ever believe this."

"So what? What matters is that something supernatural, or someone very loving, reminded us of what is important, don't you think?"

I nodded, "Brian, I'll take a picture of the rug, and then you take a picture, OK?"

As I raced from the room to get the camera, Brian continued to eye Etta's rug and called to me, "That Etta must have been a very wise woman. And she is scaring the crap out of me. The next time you go to Crownpoint, I'm going with you."

We each took a photo of the Crystal weaving and loaded the images onto Brian's computer. In disbelief, we looked at the photos side-by-side, and then at each other.

"You've got to be kidding me!" Brian remarked to his screen.

The photo I took displayed "Remember why you married *him*."

His photo showed "Remember why you married *her*."

When we ran back to the living room, the rug showed only native-plant-dyed bands of gray, beige, bronze, rust, and white.

Patricia Walkow

Patricia Walkow is an award-winning author whose work was honored in the 2016 William Faulkner Literary Competition. A full-length biography, *The War Within, the Story of Josef*, won four first-place awards in national and international competitions. She writes short stories and essays and has contributed to both online and in-print newspapers and magazines. Her work appears in over a dozen anthologies. The most recent anthology she contributed to and edited, *Love, Sweet to Spicy*, won a 2019 1st place award from New Mexico Press Women and 2nd place from National Federation of Press Women. Ms. Walkow is a former systems manager and editor emeritus of *Corrales MainStreet News*. She is a member of the Corrales Writing Group, SouthWest Writers, New Mexico Press Women, and The National Federation of Press Women. She lives in Corrales, New Mexico with her husband, cats, and one very spoiled dog.

Living Springs Publishers

We hope you enjoyed this book. Please let us know what you think about it. You can leave a review on the book page of our website.

Living Springs Publishers is a family owned, independent publishing company based in Centennial, Colorado. Our mission is to help authors, regardless of age or experience, share their gift of writing. Using our expertise in editing and publishing we help our clients bring their stories and manuscripts to life.

This is the third edition of our Baby Boomers Plus book. You can find information about our contests and buy our books at www.LivingSpringsPublishers.com.

Made in the
USA
Monee, IL